Contents

CONTENTS

A Life of Learning 87

INTRODUCTION

Sisyphus Syndrome

Psychiatry: A mindset typical of a stress-driven type 'A' person, who obtains no gratification from accomplishing the difficult goals he or she places upon himself or herself.
Concise Dictionary of Modern Medicine

This book is for entrepreneurial leaders willing to risk acting differently. It's easy to talk about change, but taking action needs courage. Many leaders today are like Sisyphus of Greek legend, doomed to forever roll a rock up a hill, only to have it fall down again. If this is your experience, then this book is for you.

Those of us who start businesses do so for various reasons: to give us freedom, to create value, satisfaction and wealth. Many of us get more than we bargain for. We soon find ourselves mired in complexity and overburdened by details. Difficult conversations are postponed and then avoided. Resentment festers. Companies lose sight of their purpose. Delegation seems impossible. We wrestle with tasks we have to do, instead of enthusiastically engaging in activities we want to do.

Small Shifts will not give you 'one-size-fits-all tips for success.' There is a big difference between knowing what to do—and doing it. Instead, *Small Shifts* will stimulate your own thinking around generating new possibilities for a better future. The book's intention is to give you a new perspective from which to take a series of actions—small actions. Wholesale change causes resistance. If you've ever tried to sell an entrepreneurial course of action to a hidebound bureaucracy, then you'll know how the status quo resists the new.

This book makes a case for incrementalism: small and appropriate changes that will make a big difference— without causing instant backlash. Our purpose is to move from leadership as a solo burden, to collaborative freedom.

The power of myth resides in its durability. In Chapter One we step back thousands of years to meet Sisyphus the condemned. There are many modern-day Sisyphus's in the business world. Many entrepreneurs want change, but refuse to share their burden. When no one else can be trusted to be as competent as we think we are, the metaphorical rock just gets heavier.

Chapter Two, "Hitting the wall," shows how we can become

prisoners of absolutist language. When we examine the words we use, we uncover our hidden—and not so hidden—perspectives and judgments. Clarity is the first step away from repetitive behaviors and toward generating better alternatives.

In Chapter Three, you'll learn about the iterative coaching process—*Shifting*. Most new ideas are too quickly abandoned or adopted. New ideas do not integrate into existing structures without periods of incubation, guidance, and practice. Not only large organizations are structured to resist the new. This resistance is primarily unconscious. Lip service is paid to learning: staff is sent for training only to come back with ideas or practices that are rejected by the status quo. Blame is usually heaped upon the trainer.

Resistance is a fact of life. Anyone who has ventured to start a business, or take one to a new level, has met with it. Who hasn't heard the familiar cry, "It can't be done!" Dogged determination alone doesn't cut it. In the seventeenth century, physicist Isaac Newton formulated his third law of motion, that each action has an equal and opposite reaction. The more you push your rock up the hill, the heavier it gets.

The Shifting process starts in the coaching encounter. This is a conversation where new options are allowed to surface. Next, there is a period of gestation. If waiting seems counterintuitive, you're right. It is. But it is an essential part of the clarifying process. New ideas are allowed to grow and strengthen. The next stage is an examination of what has occurred during the period of gestation. At this point a new leadership guidance encounter results in conversation with the purpose of formulating a practice: a set of behaviors or habits aimed at integrating the new protocols with the existing business structure.

Chapter Four addresses cultivating collaborative futures. Here we introduce memetic structures that are responsible for the gap between knowing what to do, and doing it. Memes (rhymes with genes) are "infectious" ideas that replicate themselves. Groups catch memes in the same way that a person catches a virus. Memes are not good or bad, but they form boundaries which can prevent groups from seeing the proverbial elephant in the room. Groups are defined by the values they subscribe to. There are the 'acceptable' values; there are imposed values; and there are real values. Individuals see the world differently based on their social conditioning and personal histories, but at the same time groups tend toward conformity, each member being influenced by others in close proximity. Too much conformity leads to groupthink—a perceptual blindness. This is as ineffective and darn-right dangerous as an air-traffic controller whose computer's gone kaput.

Belonging is a human need, yet successful collaborating is not intuitive, nor is it without risk. If a group is open to uncovering its memetic structure, it will have more self-knowledge. It will understand its real strengths and weaknesses. There are shadowy forces at work keeping memetic structures hidden. The brave individual will have the courage to self-reflect: the courageous leader will build a collaborative structure allowing for genuine learning and growth.

The Afterword is how this book came about: my own story. At one time I was a commodity trader. I was financially successful—or what other people would have described as successful, but I was unsatisfied. It was through a profound experience in a coaching relationship that I found my own way to a better future for me, the people around me, and the new business it generated. We are all unique, and what gives meaning and significance is different for each of us. Even what we value changes as we progress on our journeys toward personal and entrepreneurial development. Healthy adults continue to learn, and learning transforms us and the people with whom we interact.

Imagine climbing a hill. As we climb higher we get a better view. From higher up we see more choices. Perspectives matter. Possibilities come into focus from new points of view. When we have our attention glued to the rock, we don't have time or resources to look at fresh opportunities. Like Sisyphus, if we heroically and single-handedly try to push our rock up the hill, we soon suffer exhaustion, and exhaustion depletes our ability to see and capitalize on innovative options.

Change is an experience. It is individual to each of us. Our basic challenge in life is to confront the unknown. At one time or another, all of us have had to do something new; the first day of school; the first day on a job. These were times when we had to accept that we didn't quite know what we were getting ourselves into. We acted in the face of not knowing. We had to.

This was scary stuff, but our bravery gave us forward momentum. In business, we can either take active responsibility for ourselves—or change will be forced upon us. Today, our business world has never been so dynamic. No one knows what the future will bring. We can look to the past and rely on previous experience, or make educated guesses about the future. However, we can be sure the future will not be like the past.

If we don't push the boundaries of our thinking, we'll remain unprepared for a changing and dynamic world. This is living on borrowed time. We can try to deny change, but sooner or later it catches up with us. Many organizations have been paralyzed by new business realities. In 1962, the Beatles were told that Decca Recording Company didn't like their sound, and that guitar music was on the way out. Ken Olson, president, chairman, and founder of Digital Equipment Corporation in 1977 said, "There is no reason why anyone would want a computer in their home." "Who the hell wants to hear actors talk?" said H.M. Warner of Warner Brothers in 1927. The past is clearly not a reliable indicator of the future.

Denial can be disastrously expensive. We can prepare ourselves for what is coming by looking at our habitual responses and what is happening now. Small shifts create big effects. We'll examine this shifting in great detail.

Some of us have become financially successful, only to discover that the success we imagined doesn't feel good. Something is missing. This book addresses what that missing something is. Others of us want a different direction. We want to expand our horizons and move to more challenging and meaningful futures, but find ourselves bogged down in the day-to-day running of our businesses. We try to do it all, and all is too much. We are too busy for anything other than the stream of urgent demands thrust upon us. We find our work is out of alignment with our values. But how many of us have taken the time to look deeply at what we want? Examining what we value is critical in order to evolve toward satisfying business activities.

SEEKING SYNERGY

We all have natural talents. These get nurtured or fall into disuse. This is the law of biological atrophy. In other words, use it or lose it. Doing the wrong work distracts us from what we do best. Leaders with drive and energy to create new forms of business, or with foresight to anticipate a changing marketplace, are often unaware of how to become agents of change through other people. We start our businesses for various reasons: desire for freedom, to make things happen, to call the shots, to be in control. We may invest in our own future, but see less reason to invest in our team. Why should we? Won't we develop those who work for us and then they'll up and leave? Yes, this is possible.

There are no guarantees in business: a sure-fire way to success is a fantasy. Achievement demands risk. Highly integrated and functioning teams result from cultivation. A well-developed team where members bring their unique abilities to bear on the value and purpose of the business achieves great things.

Abraham Maslow, regarded as one of the world's foremost experts on human behavior and motivation, believed the workplace capable of developing what he called synergy, where genuine individual and group positive development simultaneously occurs. He wrote that our talents clamor to be used. When they go unused, apathy and dissatisfaction follow. Maslow's ideas were years ahead of their time and informed the work of business experts Peter Ducker, Jim Collins, Stephen Covey, and many others.

Now more than ever, businesses are waking up to the economic necessity of understanding how people in groups interact. Businesses with staying power understand group dynamics and respect for the individual. Treating other people well has been the remedy to strife and divisiveness since the dawn of humankind. Positive collaborative environments are the bedrock of functional businesses.

There must be space for people to contribute their uniqueness. Who hasn't seen gifted people well-developed in one area of expertise with a rudimentary grasp or complete ignorance of other areas? It is easy to fall victim to the expertise fallacy. We imagine those who excel in one area excel at everything. To be a great golfer means only to be great at golf. There may be an opportunity cost here. The golfer hasn't had time to develop other life skills. We live in a world that values specialization. This can cause pain and suffering in the workplace. Shutting people down from contributing a wider range of talents destroys group cohesion.

LEADERSHIP IS NOT MANAGEMENT BY CONSENSUS

Collaboration, though, is not management by consensus. It is about working together effectively, recognizing and integrating differences. This is easier said than done, as we shall see. Incremental changes in human interaction enable us to climb the hill and see more of the territory. This book does not advocate for management by consensus, where each person has an equal and democratic vote in the process of decision-making. Management by consensus is a recipe for gridlock. Few businesses can afford this.

Collaboration lets each person contribute what they do best. It allows for participation, growth, and effectiveness. Technical skills are important, but not the most important attribute of a team member. Most technical skills can be acquired by curious, intelligent, and enthusiastic people, people who are willing to learn. It is this attribute that has lasting value, and must be encouraged. This is not a utopian vision.

Small, incremental shifts move us along a continuum from the burden of overwhelming responsibility toward a freer and more satisfying future through partnership with others.

Like change, collaborative leadership requires courage. Courage is not a word often used in the workplace, but without it no enterprise will last. We shall have more to say on this topic. Everybody can improve what he or she does. Willingness to learn is not so much a skill as a way of being. To move from "have to," to "want to" is a worthwhile achievement. The drive to achieve harnesses our energy toward a purpose, but overdrive leads to exhaustion. And then we're doomed like Sisyphus, forever repeating the same fruitless task.

CHAPTER ONE

The Lone Leader: Sisyphus

Sisyphus was not the most ethical of leaders. He seduced his niece and usurped his brother's throne. He believed he was as powerful as the gods— and this got him into trouble. So who was Sisyphus? Most stories agree that Sisyphus was the first king of Corinth. Some say he was father of Odysseus, and promoted navigation and commerce. He was also crafty and deceitful. He violated the laws of hospitality by killing and eating his guests.

The rock fable goes like this. One day Sisyphus was looking at the sky and saw a magnificent eagle carrying a young woman in its claws. Sometime later, Asopus, the river god, came to King Sisyphus, distressed that his daughter was missing. Sisyphus, apparently gifted with the ability to tell an ordinary eagle from a god transformed into one, told Asopus what he had seen. The river god went to Zeus, and demanded his daughter back.

Zeus wanted to know how Asopus found out his daughter was with him. When Zeus learned who had exposed him, he was mad as only a Greek god can be. He ordered Death to carry Sisyphus off to the underworld. But Sisyphus—being the clever sort of fellow he was—outwitted Death by chaining him up. This caused a big problem. No one was dying and the world was getting overcrowded.

Finally the gods sent Ares, god of war, to sort things out. Ares unchained Death and delivered Sisyphus to Zeus, who condemned him to the underworld. However, before Sisyphus left he instructed his wife not to make the customary sacrifices. In other words: 'Honey, forget the taxes'.

When Hades, god of the underworld, discovered the non-payment of Sisyphus's death duties, he came up with a half-baked plan. Hades ordered Sisyphus back to the land of the living to persuade his wife to make the required sacrifices. Sisyphus took this opportunity to stay on as King of Corinth. He laughed at the gods for their lack of strategic planning. Zeus was incandescent with rage. Sisyphus remained king until he died of old age. It was then his fate caught up with him. He found himself in Tartarus, the deepest part of the underworld reserved for special suffering and torment, and this is where the rock-rolling began.

THE PUNISHMENT

No good deed goes unpunished (origin unknown).

What does this myth tell us about ourselves today? As entrepreneurs and business leaders, we shoulder great responsibility. These demands can be overwhelming. Each of us has a metaphorical rock which is the sum of the demands we face. However, these same demands can make us stronger, and more effective. Many of us suffer the dark night of the soul when we awaken in the small hours to wonder, 'What in Hades are we up to?' What once gave us energy and enthusiasm can easily turn into a debilitating burden.

Winston Churchill said of writing a book: "To begin with, it is a toy and an amusement; then it becomes a mistress, and then it becomes a master, and then a tyrant." How true this is of any new enterprise. But this is only half the quote. He goes on to write of killing the monster and flinging it out to the public. Achievement requires struggle. There comes a time when we may feel we are condemned to forever repeat the same series of fruitless tasks. We have habitual conversations that go nowhere. There is no time to learn, and problems are treated with tired and ineffective solutions.

Entrepreneurship is a whole-life approach to living. We must seek the rewards along unfamiliar paths. To make room for new choices, we have to discard ineffective practices. Change is more pressing when we are mired in frustration and failure. Vantage point matters.

Client and entrepreneur Jon had a dilemma. He was losing sight of the vision he wanted for his enterprise. One part of his brainchild was so successful it took all of his time and energy. His vocational school was achieving its mission, growing and very profitable. The school provided valuable opportunities for welfare recipients allowing them to ease their way into the workforce. Exams were rigorous, but graduation rates high. This was no mean feat.

In the midst of such success, Jon made the decision to sell. He realized that this profitable enterprise was getting in the way of his bigger vision to create and administer Allied Healthcare Certification. The school program was funded by local and state governments. Although the school was achieving its mission and attracted funding, administration was a nightmare. The funding was contingent upon successful graduation and job placement rates. In order to achieve this goal, the students needed an extraordinary amount of time-consuming care. The school was sucking energy away from the core business of certification.

Giving up something known and profitable to make way for new opportunity was not easy, but it was the right choice. Jon sold the school in order to focus on the certification business.

Once Jon put all of his energy into the core business, it began to grow exponentially. When he sold Allied Healthcare Certification, its growth rate was nearly 40 percent. Jon's courage and clarity of vision took him from burden to freedom.

Meaningful choices are hard to make. But they become almost impossible when we are unclear about what we want to keep— and what we need to get rid of. When we hold on too long through unthinking habit, fear of the unknown or misplaced sentimentality, we are punished. An organization that tolerates harmful behavior gets what it deserves.

THE ROCK: BURDEN OR GIFT?

Is your metaphorical rock a burden, or a freeing agent of growth? The rock is what tests us. It is the sum of our responsibilities, problems, achievements, desires, and needs. The rock symbolizes what needs to be done. It can push us forward into new and unfamiliar territory.

The rock is achievement in the work we do. Do we hold on tightly to it? Does the idea of sharing cause us anxiety? Do we think no one else will be as competent as ourselves? At one extreme it is an overwhelming burden. But what if we are not to be crushed by it? What if this rock is either just the right size for us, or we can get help from others who are trustworthy and competent?

The rock helps us discover our real aptitudes. The rock engages us. This is where we roll up our sleeves and do the work. Engagement with the rock is not theory, it's what happens when we confront and work within our demand space.

The rock allows us to use our capabilities, to live up to our potential. It is what the gymnasium is to the athlete. It's not just a training ground for the event; it is both the training ground and the event.

THE HILL

The hill is friction. It resists our efforts. Friction shows up in a variety of ways, such as competitors, unreasonable client demands, and regulators who may divert us and slow our forward momentum. Our businesses live within a web of collective actions: buying, selling, manufacturing, service providing, regulating, complying, researching, policing, infrastructure building, operating, managing, persuading, creating, innovating, managing, and leading. The interrelationships of all these actions make up the business ecosystem. There are actors and actions that help smooth the path to our purpose, and others that cause resistance. And there are hidden sources of friction: a series of missing conversations within our organization.

Are the people we work with sources of friction, or assets? Maybe they're a bit of both. And what is our part in all of this? What are we cultivating? Are we investing time, money, and effort in the long-term development and effectiveness of our teams? Or do we leave them to muddle through by themselves? Would we rather believe that a Band-Aid solution such as better technology will suffice?

Some resistance is self-inflicted. Without risk there is no reward. If we insist on the tried-and-true, we miss the gifts change can bring to our business environment. Friction may be a mindset. Genuine progress requires us to bring to light and examine what is hidden. This is a starting point for our companies to open to learning, flexibility, and resilience. We can make the hill easier to climb or make it not so steep.

SISYPHUS AS ENTREPRENEUR

Entrepreneurs are creative. Most people aren't able to realize value and create something from nothing. While he lived above ground, Sisyphus pushed his limits. He is like the person who creates new products and services; who rebuffs naysayers; who is not afraid to fail because he or she will learn along the way. Sisyphus has the energy to start again. However, this is not without its downside. If he's equal to the gods, he sees himself as superior to mere mortals. His burden is too precious to share. This attitude of superiority doesn't allow him to risk collaboration, so he can only shoulder his burden alone.

Our culture resists risk. In school we are not rewarded for learning from failure. We are rewarded for compliance, for getting the right answer fast. Entrepreneurs are driven by their love of creation; their passion to achieve something of significance and value that people will buy at a price they can afford. Successful enterprises are not born fully formed. They need to be cultivated. Perfectionism limits growth. The perfectionist attitude cannot tolerate untidiness. It must always be right. But the messy world is not like this. For the entrepreneur, so-called failure is learning in disguise. Mistakes are a necessary road to learning.

Software companies expect to release updates to their imperfectly released applications.

From personal experience I know that commodity traders expect to lose on occasion. Venture capitalists expect to fail most of the time. They need only a few successes. When we avoid the possibility of failure, we may never live up to our potential. This is what the poet Henry David Thoreau meant by the mass of people leading lives of quiet desperation. Without risk we are stuck doing the same old thing and fantasizing about what might have been.

IT'S LONELY AT THE TOP

Since the beginning of time, being part of a group meant survival. We hunted together. We gathered together. Banishment was the ultimate punishment. As we developed, group cohesion was necessary in times of war. But we found that trade was a better alternative to war. Commerce allowed us to develop higher and safer levels of prosperity.

The myth of the solo, heroic individual is still a strong idea in America. We focus on the exceptional business leader or sports star. We do this at the expense of supporting team members. Yet no one operates in a vacuum.

We function in relation to other people. We need other people to help us move our rock forward. Collaborative skills, though, are still rare in many companies. Since its first publication in 1997, Daniel Goleman's *Emotional Intelligence* has been read by thousands of people. But there is a significant gap between understanding the need for interpersonal communication skills and practicing them to mastery.

New leaders imagine others have the same values as themselves. This is a mistake. Leadership by example is a double-edged sword. If the leader has integrity, foresight, and the maturity to make informed decisions, this is well and good. But for the novice who has leadership and responsibility thrust upon her, ability to delegate and draw out the capabilities of the team probably won't come naturally. Her attention will be on triaging urgent tasks. This overburdened and overwhelmed leader may make clumsy attempts at delegation. When employees run into difficulties, she judges them harshly. She has high standards, and expects others to be as enthusiastic as she is. Is this realistic? Do other members of the team have the same risk-reward profile? Probably not.

Most of us spend our careers being judged based on our own achievements. We may not be teachers or mentors.

We are doers. We don't understand that other people's motivations are different from ours. Situations usually have to deteriorate dramatically before we can reach out for help. But we needn't wait for catastrophe. The secret to effective and sustainable change is to understand the multiple points of view of our current situation and then make small, appropriate, and incremental shifts over time.

VIRTUOUS CIRCLE

A leader without followers is a like geyser in the Sahara—a mirage. If you don't have followers, you're not a leader. Leaders lead, but so do ideas and causes. Leaders instill confidence in their followers, but followers give leaders their power. That is a virtuous circle.

Followers follow because they have confidence the leader has the resources and integrity to do the right thing. The buck has to stop somewhere. The leader is ultimately responsible and accountable to make decisions based on understanding the state of affairs. Leaders will not always know what to do. An authentically confident leader admits to not knowing, and seeks help when needed.

The pseudo-leader pretends to know everything. The idea of admitting ignorance is anathema. To develop authentic leadership, this fear needs to be overcome. And overcoming fear is a process best approached incrementally in a safe environment.

Entrepreneurial leaders are able to tolerate ambiguity, but temporary uncertainty will cause anxiety in others. There are powerful forces at play urging people to continually prove themselves. This extreme individualism gets in the way of collaborative effort. It sets up internal strife and unnecessary competition in the place of cooperation. Cooperation is not a course of study in school. To some extent, it shows up in team sports but this rarely translates into how people connect within collaborative work environments.

All of us have blind spots. However, collaborative groups who work in an open environment can neutralize any one person's individual delusions. Dictators surround themselves with sycophants. As leaders, we may not fully realize the potential of those around us, those who can help lighten our load, or even that our load can be lightened. Collaboration is a higher level of functioning. It makes room for everyone's point of view, new insights and behaviors save it and this instills real confidence.

EXPERTISE TRAP

Does this sound familiar? "We can't change now! We've already put money and effort into this!" Who hasn't heard this desperate cry to rationalize poor choices? Hard work—though necessary for success—does not equal value. Do we have the courage to throw away those things we have worked hard for when they no longer serve us? However, our habits developed over time, so it's unrealistic to change them in an instant. But becoming aware of habitual responses allows us to lay the groundwork for change.

Abraham Maslow wrote, "If all you have is a hammer, everything looks like a nail." We can be trapped by our own expertise. We resist considering alternatives when we fear the consequences of what we are about to do, or when we have no clear idea of what a better way could look like.

Resistance is a barrier to recognizing what is ending. Discarding our hard-won expertise in the light of new realities threatens self-perception. It takes courage to look at how our behavior may be contributing to our situation. Flexible leaders are able to abandon irrelevant expertise: Threatened individuals blame others when things go wrong. Impatience and anger follows. Resistance manifests as ignoring necessary but difficult conversations. We resist real change when we want immediate results, and our expectations are detached from reality. However, when we pay attention to our responses, resistance can be our teacher.

When we try to resist resistance, it has a nasty habit of making things worse. Reluctance hardens in the face of a head-on assault. But a small shift in perspective allows us to change the conversation and tighten the focus on what we're doing. And from this new perspective, incremental change becomes possible.

TOO BUSY TO CHANGE

Sisyphus knows what he will be doing tomorrow. He will be doing exactly the same thing as he did today. He will be all alone, struggling and straining. He will work hard repeating endless toil, safe in the knowledge that he won't have to change.

Safety and growth are on opposite ends of a continuum. The more we move toward one, the more we move away from the other. Anxiety drives people to grasp at answers—even before the question is asked.

When a rabbit experiences extreme fear it freezes. In the wild this has a camouflaging advantage. Predators miss what stays still. Now change the context. The rabbit is in the path of an oncoming 4 x 4. Result: instant ex-bunny. Old habits are useless in the face of new challenges.

Are we bunnies in the face of the unknown? Some of us are. Contemplating change can be frightening. But we can't let fear of an unfamiliar future paralyze us. Some fear may even be good for us, because it shows what we need to pay attention to. However, too much fear and we'll be doing the same joyless tasks day after day.

The fearless person is out of touch with reality. Reckless behavior ends in tears— or something much worse. How about a banking crisis? On the other hand, courage is acting in the face of fear. Courageous acts don't need to be earth shattering, or even visible to other people. But without the courage to move from familiar territory we will continue to batter our heads against the wall.

Small acts of courage add up. Moreover, courage is contextual and subjective. What one person can do easily may be a brave act for someone else. It matters a lot where you're coming from and what situation you find yourself in. Too much fear and you demonstrate the bunny effect.

But initially overwhelming situations can be managed. A small shift toward acknowledging there is a problem is a significant and courageous step. Think about how you respond to difficult choices. Is your default position to retreat or advance? Maybe you can tolerate sitting with your dilemma— and seeing what happens?

FEAR OF BEING FOUND OUT

Our basic human need is for safety. If we feel we will be harmed for taking responsibility for our own behavior and actions, then we will continue to behave in inauthentic ways. There is a temptation to hide behind a mask of professionalism. In fact, fear of discovery, that we are less qualified, less able, less intelligent than we appear to be, is a common theme that comes up time and again in private coaching sessions.

The amateur is often sneered at as being less than professional. However, the word amateur comes from the Latin word to love. Amateurs do it for love, professionals do it for money. Entrepreneurs blend the two, but at any one time what we are doing may not look professional to the outsider. Musicians may need thousands of hours of practice to achieve mastery. The desire for instant accomplishment is endemic, but deep mastery takes time and a certain level of humility. Rushing leads to superficial understanding. Confidence comes with attention and practice.

We can't feel confident about something we haven't done before. No one can tell us to be confident; we earn confidence through doing. Yet many business environments are so competitive that to be vulnerable is to invite ridicule. These unhealthy conditions breed pretense.

We can look at businesses in terms of their level of health or neuroticism, and the psychological health of those who run them and work within them. Healthy businesses provide security for people to participate and learn.

Safety needs will always trump exploration and growth needs for most employees. Entrepreneurs, on the other hand can be comfortable not knowing all the answers immediately. Essentially, this is a creative mindset. It allows space for something different to emerge.

Appetite for risk is contingent upon incentives, resources, consequences, and prohibitions. Workplace structures matter. Think about that word en-*courage*-d: a process of cultivating strength, fortitude, and active ability. Team members should be encouraged to genuinely contribute.

A safe environment allows people to express constructive opinions knowing they won't be harmed even when those opinions are unpopular. Actually creating such a structure might seem as likely as a hit musical about the tax code, but safety is foundational. Without a safe environment, innovation will die on the vine. And that's the problem. So many companies are suffering from *infectious repetitis*—the same conversations, talking about change but unable to effect it—the same in-the-box ideas endlessly repeating; the same injunctions to do more, and more, and more of the same.

CHAPTER TWO

Hitting the Wall

We live trapped, between the churned-up and examined
past and a future that waits for our work.
Anna Freud

How much is too much? When does it make sense to give up some responsibility and delegate? Do we have to wait until we are crushed by the weight of our rock? Letting go is the most difficult part of any decision. The reasons why we don't—or won't— delegate are legion. "If you want something done right, do it yourself." "If you want something done, give it to a busy person." We've all heard these attempts to justify expediency. This sort of helpfulness comes at a price. When we help others by doing their work, it increases our burden. Even worse, it leaves the person we are supposedly helping feeling incompetent. This can lead to a downward spiral. We may feel gratified by helping. We tell ourselves we are achieving the overall goal. But we are not; we are not the solo-heroic leaders we think we are. It takes more courage to delegate than it does to burn yourself out by trying to do it all. Sooner or later you'll hit the wall.

It's true there are times when it makes sense not to delegate, when we must step in and take over. However, let's ask ourselves the tough questions. Let's examine our motivations and consider the likely outcomes of our behavior. When we help by taking away responsibilities from others, we create a culture of dependency. Think about this. Are you creating a structure of dependency or cultivating autonomy, competence, and participation? At some point you'll need to give up the short-term fix of doing it all yourself, and make an investment in creating a supporting structure for change. It's the structure that matters. Big changes don't happen by gritting your teeth in a Sisyphean effort. Willpower is finite. Just telling yourself to behave differently doesn't work.

The environment needs to change, in small increments. Think about changing a diet. If you have tempting, high-calorie foods in the refrigerator, you're likely to snack. Out of sight is out of mind. Replacing those foods with more healthy ones creates a different environment. You may still have impulses to snack but you have limited your options. How can you change your environment to foster support and learning rather than instant task completion? Think about it.

EXTREMISTS IN THE WORKPLACE

"This is not just serious, it's dire! I'm overwhelmed, I'm overburdened. I feel devastated." Do you hear this sort of extreme language?

Helen is CEO of Dangerous Fashion Designs. She complains to me that her bookkeeper never listens. I reflect back to her the language she uses.

"Never!" I say. "Does she never listen to you? How long has she been working for you?"

"Two years," replies Helen.

"In two years, has Janet ever listened to you—even once?"

"Well, yes, but there are times when she cuts me off."

"So there are times when she does listen?"

"Yes."

"So tell me about the times when she does—and the ones when she doesn't."

We talk further. The situation now becomes less extreme. I suggest it could be that Helen has a part in this situation herself. We discover that Janet recognizes Helen's tendency to repeat herself. Helen repeats herself because she thinks Janet doesn't understand. Nevertheless, Helen has just judged Janet as never listening. Janet judged Helen as not trusting her to understand the first explanation. The relationship is polarized.

We dig deeper into "what is," and more options start to open up. Over time, perspectives shift.

Helen becomes aware of her extremist language and with support and practice begins to make changes. Eventually she learns to communicate more functionally with Janet, and from this new place of understanding the relationship improves significantly.

Effective communicators understand the importance of word choice. The language we use creates reality. Extreme words create either a false sense of anxiety-provoking alarm, quasi-importance, and drama, or they become overused slogans bled of meaning. When words are detached from practical concerns they become the fluff of content-free conversations.

Extremist language is an attempt to convey a need for action or to control a complex environment. There are better ways. Without taking the time to understand what is happening — right now— all we have are judgments and rules.

When we don't pay attention to our use of radical language, we can easily miss the effect it has on those who hear it. When someone describes herself as devastated, what does this communicate? Is it terminal? Is recovery possible? Is she really devastated or just disappointed? And could this disappointment indicate something amiss about her expectations? Is your default style to observe and listen, or is it to swell and crowd out any space for other voices?

UNREALIZED POTENTIAL

Business is a conversation. It is a web of collaborative conversations. Each year, businesses waste vast sums of money through miscommunication. Learning to understand our own communication styles and how others perceive us is the first step toward greater effectiveness. Open leadership will want to maximize capacity and create space for contribution. When all voices are not given scope, we leave profit on the table. Who can afford unrealized human potential? Conversation is a process of give and take—asking and listening.

Many business hierarchies are structured to rely on positional status, and these form a barrier to understanding prevailing conditions. Open leadership listens. Leadership will want to understand what's happening at the place of customer contact. It will want to understand the perceptions of employees at all levels, not just those who have been anointed. There is no place for an inner circle in a small organization; in any organization.

Entrepreneurs know that expertise is acquired in the process of creating. An authority is able to demonstrate applied knowledge and proficiency. The words "author" (one who creates something) and "authority" are related. The author-as-creator understands process. Authoritarian leadership is often defensive and cannot tolerate mistakes. When a blunder occurs (and who among us hasn't made at least one?), it's always someone else's fault. The authoritarian blames, but authority seeks understanding. Authoritarian leadership believes in absolute and constant control. Authoritarian and collaborative leaders are at opposite ends of a behavioral spectrum.

Safety is necessary, but too much safety leads to paralysis.

Lack of all safety leads to recklessness and bravado. Understanding individual worldviews (our perceptions and what we consider to be normal) gives us insight into what limits —and promotes— new possibilities. The world is made real to us through the stories we tell ourselves, and the language we use.

DAVID'S DILEMMA

David inherited the family business, General Tension. David never expected to be running the firm. He always thought of himself in different terms. You could say he was a reluctant businessman. His dad had built the business from scratch into a profitable concern. Along with the business, David inherited some long-term employees, to whom his dad had given each a minor share in General Tension.

David shows up in the coaching session with a list of complaints. He's trying to lead, but no one is following. He says he's overwhelmed, and I find out that David's inherited partners are paid twice what they could reasonably expect to be paid on the open market. Dad was appreciative and generous, but this has become a headache for his son. David is in a difficult situation. He's getting no respect from his new partners. In fact, they're belittling him. They say he doesn't know much about the business. To some extent, that's true. David can't articulate exactly what they do. He says it's too technical to describe to someone not in the business.

He's the new boss, and without other resources he's adopted an authoritarian style. This of course makes matters worse. His management style is defeating group integration. It's creating a divisive them-and-us situation. War has been declared at General Tension. David is exasperated. He sees his dilemma in stark terms. For him, there are only two extreme choices: suffer things as they are or quit.

David uses the word "trapped" to describe how he feels. I ask him what he wants. At first this question perplexes him. He's never slowed down enough to think deeply about his real desires. Eventually he says he wants a month off. He wants to step away from the business. This moment of clarity doesn't come immediately. He throws up objections to his own desires. It's a struggle. How can he possibly leave the operations to the bozos (as he refers to his partners) out back? Who else would pay him as much as he's getting now?

Nevertheless, this is the moment the compass points north and our coaching sessions find their true direction. David becomes clear about his dilemma.

DONKEY DECISIONS

A donkey is tethered midway between a pail of water and a stack of hay. It's hungry and thirsty. If it moves toward the water it will die of hunger. If it moves toward the hay it will die of thirst. The fourteenth-century French philosopher Jean Buridan made this ancient paradox popular. It's also known as Buridan's Ass. The story that is, not any part of Buridan's anatomy. Of course, this is a hypothetical tale designed to promote discussion around action, risk, and free will. The dilemma assumes that the donkey will move toward whichever attraction is closest. Since it can make no logical decision which to choose, it stays where it is and consequently dies of hunger and thirst. This is the cost of doing nothing, and this is precisely the situation David finds himself in.

Change for David means he risks losing financial security. If he doesn't change, he remains dependent and guarantees himself a life of misery. But the upside (if it can be called that) is he will continue to benefit from affluence although he will be unhappy. From the outside what David should do may appear easy, but for the person who's making such a decision there is more going on than meets the eye. Rarely are decisions black and white. Obvious solutions don't address hidden complexity. Without digging deeper into what's happening, we become victims of unintended consequences.

David's situation is not unusual. Dissatisfaction can lead to despair— or it can be the springboard into a new future. There comes a time when we realize what we're doing is not working. The skills and talents we've acquired have brought us this far, but we need something different— new ways of thinking, seeing, and behaving to get us to where we want to go.

The good news is David will shift away from his defensive and autocratic style and move toward becoming a collaborative leader. But his journey requires ongoing guidance. He will need to be clear about the real dilemma he is facing. What sort of language is he using to describe his situation? Is he overdramatizing it? The first small shift toward reality-based progress is to understand the present. And this is a collaborative process.

HEY! I'M DOING THE TALKING HERE

One person holds the floor, while the rest of the group knows enough to keep silent until the monologue is over. In such a scenario, the facilitating language of collaborative leadership and inclusion is absent. "Business Theater" has no other purpose than to communicate who is in charge.

Language is used for purposes other than to facilitate ideas and actions. Language includes or excludes. We can choose to use the encompassing "we," instead of the alienating "I" and "you people."

Language creates reality. Absolutist and dramatic language indicates limiting beliefs. We know, however, that small shifts from extremist positions can open up unexpected potential. Absolutist language seeks immediate closure. It judges. It's a demonstration of power. It doesn't want discussion and isn't open to new or alternative perspectives. Of course, there is a time and place for ending discussions. But in general, absolutist language shuts the door, digs in its heels, covers its ears, and refuses to budge.

Authoritarian leadership rests on power and threat of consequences. There are times when this is necessary. Judges can send people to prison. Military commanders require absolute obedience from subordinates. Entrepreneurs can fire their staff. Is it possible to be a successful authoritarian leader? The answer is yes, up to a point. It is certainly possible to have financial success— for a time.

Nevertheless, authoritarian leadership in commerce has so many flaws that it's the least likely management style to lead to long-term success. But what is success? The answer varies by individual. If success means creating something of personal meaning and significance, then authoritarian success is a very high-risk proposition.

WORLDVIEWS

This is not the view from outer space. A worldview is how we see the world through the mesh of our social and cultural conditioning, education, and experience. Our worldview determines what we pay attention to, and what we ignore. It determines how we think, what we think about, and what we consider normal. Multiple worldviews help to overcome the limitations of monoculture. It can both be efficient and blinding when everyone in our environment has the same values, the same education, and the same motivations. Need for explanation will be unnecessary, but there will be no one to see the approaching disaster. The mono-cultural worldview will not notice what it's not trained to look for. No one will be able to point out that the Emperor has no clothes.

Think of how an architect looks at a building. She will see it in a different way from a construction contractor, or a real estate investor, or someone looking for a family home. Different people pay attention to different things depending on their motivations and the structural environments they find themselves in. Our worldview limits us to what we pay attention to.

To attend to one thing is to ignore something else. When we focus in order to see something more clearly, we pay a price of not attending to something else. This is a perceptual opportunity cost. Experts have deep yet narrow knowledge. Generalists have shallower knowledge, but a greater awareness of context. Progress and value come from the collaboration of contributing worldviews. Leadership must be aware of the context in which her organization operates.

The isolated leader may be a legend in his own mind. When leaders surround themselves with sycophants, they don't have a chance to correct ineffective behavior. Mistakes are never mentioned. However, with input from a range of voices the collaborative leader will be more reality-based. When we join forces, we uncover previously hidden resources in other people. We benefit from their know-how. When we listen in order to reach for an understanding of other worldviews, we demonstrate openness and respect.

A diplomat may not be able to fathom the customs of foreign nations, yet he can still respect that they are different and have meaning and value for those who practice them. And by observation he may get ideas of transferrable value. Acceptance (not necessarily adoption) of other worldviews benefits us by cognitive diversity. When we do not try to impose our own autocratic regime on others, we make space for genuine collaboration. What is our behavior? Are we imposing by telling, or are we seeking to discover by asking?

Today it is not enough to have a nineteenth-century mechanistic mindset that simply looks for efficient goal completion. Educator Sir Ken Robinson wrote that creativity will be as necessary in the twenty-first century as literacy was in the twentieth. The ability to observe, learn, listen, seek novel experiences, communicate, reflect, collaborate, and understand are fundamental attributes for survival, prosperity and beyond. What is beyond survival and prosperity? The answer is significance and satisfaction. But these may seem distant qualities to someone toiling forever up the same Sisyphean hill.

THE INVISIBLE GORILLA

Can you recall the last three people you saw today? What were they wearing? You probably did encounter three people—all of them wearing clothes. So how come you can't remember what you saw? The answer is that we only pay attention to what matters to us. We ignore the rest. A well-known study on inattentional blindness is the Invisible Gorilla Test. Daniel Simons of the University of Illinois at Urbana-Champaign, and Christopher Chabris of Harvard University, asked participants to look at video of two teams of players passing a basketball. One team was in white shirts and the other in black. The subjects (those watching the video) were asked to count either aerial passes or bounces. At the end of the video, they were then asked if they had noticed anything unusual. Fifty percent of participants failed to notice a person dressed in a gorilla suit walking through the middle of the scene beating his chest.

Other worldviews help us overcome inattentional blindness. Questions are far more useful than merely requesting information. An answer to a question is a different animal from a response. Questions stimulate thinking. And the right question, at the right time, in the right context, is the catalyst to shift our attention to what's happening at present and so discover what we're missing.

LET'S PRETEND TO BE SUCCESSFUL

Flat Designs was going through a bad patch. Michael, the president, thought he did a good job of communicating the situation to his employees. They needed to tighten their belts. There would be no bonuses again this year. And this was all for the good of the company. Michael could see light at the end of the tunnel. He assured everyone there would be no layoffs.

At first, everyone understood: what was good for the company was good for the employees. But despite the grim finances of the company, Michael couldn't resist acquiring a white Maserati GranTurismo S. It made him feel like a winner. Michael's image of success was not aligned with the reality of Flat Designs. He had transgressed an unwritten law.

He parked his car several streets away in order to hide the fact that there were enough funds for a least one person to enjoy luxury. The employees found out in the end, but that is another story.

Secretiveness breeds distrust. This doesn't mean that everyone should know everything. That would violate boundaries of individual and professional privacy. Transparency adds importance to the leadership role. It doesn't mean being so open your brains fall out. Transparency is not about giving away power. It provides clear explanations of what and why things are being done, thereby fostering participation.

Michael hit the wall (not in his car, thankfully). His problem came from his perception. Only by experiencing his own values clash and the damage it did to the team did he seek leadership guidance. And when he goes through the Shifting process (see next chapter), he learns to be a more unifying leader and starts to put the company back on track.

URGENT!!!

When Yogi Berra was asked the time, he said, "You mean now?" In the hectic rush of day-to-day living there is little time to slow down to be here and now. Now is ignored. We are distracted. The more pressure builds, the less time we have for reflection. Let's cram more tasks into fewer hours. Let's work longer hours. We'll get more done, right? This sort of thinking sees humans as machines. The more we work, the more fatigued we become. Keep up this hectic pace long enough and we end up with damaged health. And do tired leaders make good decisions?

Hardly. There are countless examples of disasters caused by decision-makers pulling long hours. There are studies showing that lack of sleep cumulatively lowers IQ. Go long enough without adequate rest and you have the mental acuity of a drunk. Airline companies instruct passengers to put on their own oxygen masks before helping others. If we don't take care of our personal abilities to make decisions, no one else will do it for us. There is a lot riding on the decisions we make.

Parkinson's Law states that work expands to fill the time available for its completion. We are creatures of habit. Habit conceals. Shakespeare likened habit to a monster "who all sense doth eat." It's true our habits operate below the level of consciousness; no thinking is required. Habit is a cloak that monks wear. We can feel warm and secure wrapped in our habit. The more other people have the same habit, the less visible it is. And what we don't see, we can't change. Busyness for its own sake is a habit well supported in business. Most of us live lives of constant interruption. Everything is urgent and should have been done yesterday. Tasks mount up. We wish for a time when we have a clear desk and can focus on the direction we want to pursue, but that time never arrives. We are time-poor.

Clarity requires we master distractions; step back from the

day-to-day demands of business to see what we value and how our values change over time. If this looks like a vicious circle—it is. We need time to examine where we are, think about alternatives, evaluate them, and act. But in the everyday rush, all of this 'thinking time' seems like a luxury. It isn't. It's a necessity. If you can make time for a meeting, you can make time for thinking.

What once was acceptable may have become unacceptable. Did you notice how that came about? At what point did the problem start. Were you looking in the wrong direction? Are you still pursuing activities that once served you, but now no longer do?

Sisyphus has little time to think about what is important. He's busy rolling his rock up the hill. Habit is powerful. It can be a blessing and a curse. The sneaky thing about habits is that they are invisible to us. We don't know what we're doing. Other people have a better chance of pointing out our routine behavior if we let them. Spouses are notoriously good at this sort of thing. But we can only be aware of our habits if we are willing to be receptive. Mostly we accept criticism with as much enthusiasm as getting a parking ticket.

How can we prioritize when everything is urgent? What

are the long-term consequences of attending to the urgent and ignoring the important?

At Speed Solutions Now (SSN), Mary Sable has been charged with leadership training for managers. Experts are hired with name recognition from Ivy League schools. This pleases upper-management because it gives them a warm and fuzzy feeling that their staff is being trained by some of their own.

A half day has been allocated and all managers are required to attend. Why half a day? It's just a habit. It's what they do at SSN. The managers are attentive. They take notes. Good ideas are communicated. One month after the expensive training: no change.

Training gets "delivered." It might as well be a cardboard package offloaded to the mail room. This one-size-fits-all solution ignores the current needs of the business. It's a simple solution to a complex problem. There wasn't time to understand the managers' worldviews, nor their concerns, nor the pressing and important issues they're facing. The managers were simply shown research and given canned conclusions. There was no attempt at an integrative group follow-up.

Knowing "about" something doesn't mean it's doable; and

doing the right thing matters. Nobody likes being told what to do. When we assume learners aren't as smart as we are, we do them, and ourselves, a disservice. Learning, like leadership, is an experience. Having experience (history) and having an experience (subjective awareness of an event) are different. Having experience means we are capable because our history prepares us for what we need to do. This view is obsolete.

Research shows we do not imbibe information and simply recall it later. Our past experience may be of little use to us if we simply have acquired abstract knowledge. In a study done at the University of Hull in the United Kingdom, Geoff Lowe[1] showed the importance of context in learning. Two groups of students were given a map and asked to memorize a route from locations A to B. Twenty minutes before the learning event one group of students was given large vodka and orange juice cocktails. The other group was only given orange juice. The next day, all the students were asked to recall what they had learned. Then the students were divided into four groups. Only one group was given vodka and orange juice, and the remaining three were given just orange juice. The groups that did best were the ones who had learned and recalled in the same state. The group that learned and recalled "drunk" and the group that learned and recalled "sober" did best. Those

[1]Geoff Lowe (1980), "State dependent recall decrements with moderate doses of alcohol", *Current Psychological Research*, v. 1,

that had learned sober and recalled drunk, and those that had learned drunk and recalled sober, did worst. The conclusion is that learning is contextual and holistic.

Experience is a subjective state. It's not just what we do, but how we feel about it and how it changes us. At Speed Solutions Now, experience was discounted. Notes were taken to refer back to at a (imagined) later date, but no change in perception. There was no personal moment of insight. Real change takes an investment of time. Only by comprehending why problems exist can we start to look at how they came about and at the behaviors and assumptions that created them.

Quick fixes hit the wall fast when they impose a one-size-fits-all solution. When we seek understanding, we need to couch our communication to benefit the individual's aspirations within the group. And to understand what other people's worldviews are—and here is missing piece—we need to ask them. What a concept! *We need a different type of conversation.* But asking isn't enough; then we need to listen and respond appropriately. This is much easier said than done.

JUST GIVE ME THE ANSWER!

Expecting a simple answer to a complex question is like a broken pencil—pointless. If life were simple, all we would need is a recipe for action. All we would have to do is follow a few helpful rules and we would get what we want. Procedural thinking is great if you want to bake a cake, change a tire, or program a software app. For example, we're in the kitchen and we want to bake our cake and we have all our ingredients handy. The recipe tells us what to do. We end up with a fabulous pastry. That is a closed system. The problem is when we take a successful strategy that works well in a closed or static system and misapply it. Procedural instructions work well when we are programming computer code and are clear about the objectives and resources available. However, when we use the same static thinking in a system where change is constant, we've got the wrong tool for the job.

Albert Einstein said things should be as simple as possible—but no simpler. The leader's job is to make decisions, and this requires intelligence, time, and effort. Wanting simplistic answers is a substitute for taking responsibility for the time and hard work of looking at where we are. It ignores what is happening outside our immediate view. Because we all have blind spots, one person's view is limited, yet when group members are allowed to participate what we are doing becomes clearer.

Leaders ask, listen, think, and take action.

WISHFUL THINKING

Jane is a bookkeeper at Immovable Inc. She's doing a great job. She knows her stuff, and gets along well with other people. However, Jane never comes to meetings because she's not invited. There's much about the business she doesn't really understand. Why does she need to? She's just the bookkeeper, right?

Immovable starts to get busier. It's only a small organization. Alice, the principal, talks up the need for everyone to pitch in. She recognizes Jane's competence and imagines she can do some extra work for the company in marketing support. Jane, wanting to help, doesn't object. She even feels she might learn something. Nevertheless, there's been no space for Jane to spend time understanding the fundamentals of marketing or the greater mission of the business, let alone why customers buy.

So when problems occur, Alice blames Jane for dropping the ball. Alice is puzzled why such a previously good employee should suddenly make so many mistakes. She labeled Jane as smart and efficient and never thought much beyond that judgment. But the problem is with her resistance to looking at the situation from a developmental perspective. Alice had unrealistic expectations. Resistance denies what is.

Almost all of us will agree on the need for reinvestment in our enterprises. When it comes to doing something different, though, fear sends us backward. We become stuck. We don't see what is new because we don't recognize it for what it is: different. We translate the situation as if we understand it when, in reality, we don't understand at all. To admit we don't know is an act of courage. To reach out for support is an intelligent and practical response.

Resistance shows up in multiple ways: poor use of external financing, lack of team development, inability to self-reflect, not valuing ongoing education, ignoring the subjective experience of ourselves and those around us.

We see resistance in body posture: folded arms, turning away, pushing back from the table. We feel our own resistance in how we tighten our jaw or tense our muscles. Resistance is a bodily event: a reflex. Even though resistance is an embodied experience, it is easily missed if we are unaware of our own physical responses. Our bodies are more than vehicles for getting our heads to meetings. Each of us will experience this resistance differently.

NO VISION: DIVIDED PURPOSE

There's a problem at Radiant Light Technologies (RLT). Bob founded his company four decades ago. He's rightly proud of his achievement. There have been ups and downs, but overall the company's profitability has steadily increased. For many years, Bob was satisfied with bottom-line growth and never saw the need for—in his words—that waste-of-time vision stuff. This was until he began to think about his legacy; what all the hard work and achievement meant to him.

Through a series of conversations, Bob realizes he wants his company to be recognized as the quality design and manufacturing solution it is. He understands his brand will be the sustaining feature after he retires. However, more than 70 percent of the revenue comes from deals the company has set up to sell their products as "white label." In other words, his company's name never appears on the excellent products it makes. This is a real problem for brand recognition, and change will negatively impact the current, and profitable, relationship with their white-label resellers.

Bob has a dilemma. He needs courage to change from something that works well now to making RLT recognizable in the commercial space it occupies. Bob needs a vision that everyone can buy into.

Resistance is there from the beginning. Just to get his people together is a frustrating task. Staff is located regionally. And once they get wind of change, they make multiple excuses for not having time to get together. In fact, getting together as a group has never been a feature of RLT.

Do the regional salespeople care about Bob's legacy? No. They are making a nice living from their relationships with resellers. Why should they care? Do they understand the risk to the company of selling so much of its product to just a few resellers? Can they see a future where RLT is known for excellence in its own right? The answer is no and no: complacency rules. No vision means divided purpose.

At this point, Bob takes action and readies himself for the courageous and difficult conversations ahead of him. The first small shift is to achieve agreement to a face-to-face meeting with all staff. Not everyone will accept Bob's new structure. The complacent will have to look for other opportunities. But those who see how they can contribute will want to participate in creating a stronger company with a clear vision. Vision aligns self-interest to group purpose, and this synergistic relationship springboards achievement into another territory.

START WHERE YOU ARE

An entrepreneur was lost in the mountains of Colorado. For hours she searched for the land she was hoping to buy. Eventually, she saw an old cowboy by the side of the road. She stopped the car, rolled down her window, and asked for directions. The cowboy said he knew the place and it was quite easy to get to. The entrepreneur complained she'd been driving for hours since she left Denver and couldn't find it. The cowboy responded: "Your problem is you started in the wrong place. You should've started from here. "

It's a lot easier to talk about future goals than to take a clear-sighted look at our current situation and ask the tough questions: How did we get here? How is what we're doing serving us? And there's an even bigger question, which we'll turn to next.

CHAPTER THREE

Shifting: The Process

T he ancient sage Lao-tzu said that a journey of a thousand miles begins with a single step. That first step is a question. What do you want? Maybe you can spit out a thousand responses in a nanosecond. Probably, though, this question leaves you scratching your head. It might be so obvious you never sought to ask it, let alone spend quality time with it. How do you know the answer you give is what you want, and not what you think you should want—what other people expect you to want?

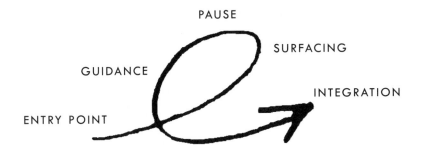

PAUSE

SURFACING

GUIDANCE

INTEGRATION

ENTRY POINT

Shifting begins at the **Entry Point**. This is the initial coaching encounter. **Surfacing** arises from these conversations where new opportunities, ways of behaving, ideas, and possible trajectories emerge. Once a new concept is recognized, we examine it further, but then allow for a period of incubation. At this point in the process we press the **Pause** button. Instead of directly confronting problems with solutions, we allow insight to integrate with our current worldview. This waiting period allows us to experience our new insight over time. This can be a rich and creative process. After the period of gestation, we enter a co-creative **Guidance** encounter. Here we reengage to examine what we have learned. During this step, we are likely to design a **Practice**; practical actions which help integrate new behaviors and nudge a small growth shift into the entire system.

Integration is complete when these new actions have been absorbed into the system and changed it. Now we have made a slight alteration that over time will result in a "new normal." When the new idea is fully integrated into the dynamic structure of the organization, the circle is complete. The whole company, its behaviors and its thinking, has now been influenced by a small shift. From this higher level of functioning, we are ready for the next shift where the iterative process is ready to begin with a new entry point.

1. ENTRY POINT

Let's imagine you and I are working together. We engage in a conversation. You talk. I listen. I'm seeking to understand your world. Our starting point could be as murky as a swamp after an oil spill. Or, you may be able to present a clearly defined dilemma. Each conversation is unique, but the initial purpose is for both of us to seek understanding and clarity. Maybe there is a difficult conversation you've been avoiding. Or, you may be outwardly successful but feeling a generalized dissatisfaction and you're not sure why. What once was acceptable has become pain, suffering, and gnashing of teeth. Perhaps your business is going into a tailspin—or growing faster than an inflating life raft. Maybe you have a mutiny on your hands? Whatever the situation, the purpose is to discover the reality of "what is." We talk. Mostly you talk, and I listen. I listen as much to what you're not saying as to what you are saying. What you say you want and what you really want may be different. At some point in our conversation we are able to articulate what it is you really want—and what you don't want. Then, we tackle that difficult opportunity-cost question: what are you willing to give up? Acquiring is always easier than discarding.

If you write down what you want today, will this be what you want tomorrow, next year, in ten years? Why not get a pen and jot down one, two or three sentences and see? Is this where you want to put your time, effort, and resources? The job of the leader is to make decisions. But there is more to this than choosing from a restaurant menu. Choosing from a predefined set of options may be the last step in a decision-making progression, but generating those possible courses of action is where the heavy lifting is done.

Is what you want something short-term, or longer-term? Is your answer in response to fixing something? Is it a management want, to maintain the status quo, or an innovation to improve what you already do? On the other hand, is it an entrepreneurial leadership want; a completely new line of work; a new business venture, or even a different state of being? Is what you want realizable? How do you know if it is—or isn't? There is great value in asking this seemingly simple what-do-you-want question. It can keep you from pushing your rock up the wrong hill. This question is the vital starting point for making a small shift in an authentic direction. Spending time here at the beginning of the journey is worthwhile.

2. SURFACING

In the process of these early conversations, new ideas typically emerge. We have now made a small shift (or series of small shifts). We have reached higher ground. From here our perspective is quite different from the entry point. We thought about what it is you want, what you don't want, and we talked about the necessary courage to let go. Only now, we look at the new shifted situation in more detail. What are the forces preventing your desired future? Between us, we can generate alternative futures.

The way you use language may be perfectly normal and invisible to you, but when we dig deeper into what some of your words mean, they open to reveal unexpected value. It's this "different" focus of attention that is illuminating. The new concept is able to surface in a safe environment of mutual trust. Your willingness to explore is the bedrock of the shifting process.

The idea is revealed. Our challenge now is to recognize it for what it can be. In general, we only see what we look for. Imagine you just bought a new car. You are likely to notice other cars of the same make and model on the road. Your attention has been directed by your experience. Limited focus may keep you from stumbling upon that new and useful idea. A benefit of working with people from different disciplines is that the group takes in a wider perspective.

Recognizing what is present is not as simple as it may seem. New ideas usually meet with resistance. If they are adopted immediately, they can become victims of the honeymoon syndrome. Marry in haste, repent at leisure. Better not get carried away. Gushing over a new idea is dangerous when we don't take into consideration the time, effort, and resources necessary to put our concept into practice. Now is the time to press the pause button. We have conceived a fresh idea, a novel course of action, or an exciting possibility. Pregnancy isn't something you want to rush. Let's incubate.

3. PAUSE

We hate to wait. We rush to appointments rather than waste a minute waiting. We know getting there early makes sense, but we just can't seem to do it. And when we do have to wait, we must distract ourselves. Maybe check out what other airline passengers are doing across the aisle. We plug ourselves in. We play games on our mobile gizmos. We listen to music. Some of us pretend to work. Others actually do work, even in coach. All this is to avoid free and unstructured time. Our knee-jerk reaction is to want tangible action now!

We are as impatient as a three-year-old who's been told to wait a few minutes before eating a cookie that's right in front of him. Action—even if it is wrong action—gives us the impression we are actually doing something. However, there is a raft of academic literature pointing to the benefits of the ability to delay gratification. Before marching off into the wilderness with our half-baked new idea, why not let it cook?

What does this mean? What is it to incubate an idea? Guy Claxton[2] coined the term "undermind" for this other way of knowing. He talks about D for deliberate mode thinking. This is our default logical and measurable way of approaching situations. Here is the problem: if we can't rationalize and explain an idea, then there is something wrong and we ignore it. D-mode thinking is fast, rational, and limited. At its extreme, it is myopic. But what about good ideas that are underdeveloped and aren't ready to see the light of day? What about concepts that need tweaking? Do we throw the baby out with the bathwater? Some of us do.

[2]Claxton, Guy, Hare brain tortoise mind: How intelligence increases when you think less.

The undermind is a slow and creative process. In order to access it you must be able to relax or turn off D-mode. Earnestness and impatience keep the contents of the undermind hidden. Pausing allows time to get in touch with this creative resource. We can—heaven forbid—play with an idea and see what comes up. Can we be playfully serious? Yes. There is a difference between being somber and being serious. Often new discoveries come at the point of mental exhaustion when there is no alternative but to stop working and recover. "Taskiness" gets in the way. Chronic overwhelm prevents creative options from surfacing. We may need to stop rushing long enough to see what's there. Scary!

Breakthroughs are made at the most unusual times. Archimedes made his discovery of the principles of hydrostatics while soaking in the bathtub. The discovery of the benzene ring came in a dream. Scientists and artists have long known that the creative process relies on letting things sit. This may seem counterintuitive in the hectic daily rush of business. Gestation allows a different part of the brain to operate. We want to have a chance to turn down the volume on the logical left brain and allow the right brain to work with our problem or insight. You've heard the expression, sleep on it. We can see situations differently in the morning. The point is we have to quiet the constant internal chatter in order to let our nonverbal imaginative and more intuitive side come to the surface. Incubating an idea may need a change of location. Switching tasks to something not requiring much brainpower helps. It seems counterintuitive, but relaxing could be more productive than furrowing your brow and concentrating harder and harder on the problem.

Let's take a break and go to the gym.

Every January people flock to the gym. They have the best of intentions. They love the idea that fit is better than flab. Consequently the gym is packed. But by February the crowd has thinned out. So here we are at the gym. Take a look around you. There are the treadmills, aerobics classes, and over there, the weight machines. But what exactly are you going to do? How long should you exercise? How much weight should you lift? The weekend warrior goes at it like a bull in a china shop and ends up injured. Good intentions without reinforcement last about as long as an ice-cream cone in a sauna. A personal trainer understands limits. Her training and experience tell her how much you should push yourself. Muscle building is more than a metaphor. When we build muscle we tear the fibers. What we do actually weakens us— initially. Next comes a period of recovery, but the muscle being stressed now has a chance to adapt to the new demands. It becomes stronger than before.

Acetylcholine is a brain chemical essential for learning. Studies have shown that there is more of this chemical in the brains of rats that worked on solving difficult problems than their couch-potato brothers and sisters. And not just rats—autopsies show that people who did "brainwork" had more neural connections than those who did manual labor. We adapt by doing. Learning is an anatomical event. We grow neuronal capabilities in response to challenges. Mental fatigue is a signal that we should do something less demanding—for a while. Like the weightlifter's progress, we need periods of rest in which to integrate new experiences. Sleep plays a major role in turning short-term memory into long-term memory. But we also need reinforcement and expertise as we continue to put down roots in our newly discovered territory.

4. GUIDANCE

New behaviors are fragile. They need cultivating. Your new behaviors and ideas will probably be resisted by a hostile workplace. You may be asked to explain yourself. Now we look at what has changed. We'll investigate what went on during the period of incubation. What new opportunities occurred to you? What was your experience like? What needs to end before something else can begin? What are the consequences of taking a difficult but necessary course of action? This part of the process is checking in and pointing out. We are now in different territory and guidance is needed to show the way. The landscape has changed. From this position we get a more appropriate view of what's happening. Without support and guidance at this point, new perspectives will probably be short-lived. We may easily slip back into old views. What are we missing?

The old and new perspectives are doing battle. Cognitive dissonance is confusion that comes from holding two conflicting ideas. We may rationalize our tightly-held views despite new evidence to the contrary. You are a rational sort of person—aren't you? We like to think we behave rationally. But we often don't. For example, you may have a strong political affiliation. It's unlikely any amount of evidence to the contrary would convince you to bat for the other team. Of course you may be one of the few exceptions. New evidence is usually discounted because it threatens self-perception. And this is true of systems, companies, teams, and other groups.

Groups of people have natural boundaries that determine what is acceptable and what isn't. Sadly, we reject what we don't understand. Before a new idea is understood and adopted, the first response is probably rejection. In general, we hold on to an image of ourselves and resist anything that will disrupt it. With a small shift, the new insight that surfaced has now had time to gestate. It has become not just an abstract idea but personal experience.

Leadership guidance looks at how the nascent behavior can integrate with the current culture: a synthesis. At this point we co-create a transitional practice. You can think of it as prototyping.

5. PRACTICE

This is where we get to try things out. Your practice is a discrete change in behavior. You begin to pay attention to things you previously ignored. Recently, a client made a small shift in where she sat in meetings. How simple is that? But it changed the dynamics. It was the right change. It came through her understanding of what she was previously doing. Instead of leading from the front and displaying her expertise, she listened and asked a few questions. She demonstrated leadership. Her presence in the room was far more effective in shifting her toward becoming an influential leader.

Your practice will be specific to your situation, but it will be a change. So what does a practice look like? You have to do something. The focus here is on doing. It may be a practice of noticing. How do other people respond to you? You may develop the practice of being genuinely curious about other points of view, and this could be the entry point into having that previously avoided conversation. Your practice could be to shake things up; be more provocative. If you want to change your culture from a group of yes-men and yes-women to one where constructive criticism is encouraged, you'll need to open up space to question destructive assent and its consequences. The acronym COIN can help guide attention during conflict. What is the Context? What do I Observe? What is the Impact? What do I Need? You'll notice your own responses.

Behave differently and you'll change the group. You'll change your self-perception. You'll change your own effectiveness. At first, you may feel like an imposter. A less judgmental way of thinking about this is to recognize your experience as unfamiliar. A practice is likely to be sustainable if it's easy to do. The secret to improvement is regularity and duration. The pianist practices her scales. The golfer goes out and swings the club. Of course everyone who swings a golf club will not become a master golfer. Context matters. We all have individual desires, strengths, and weaknesses. The importance of guidance here is that we design a practice that is aligned with your own values and aspirations. The practice must fit the person and the situation. Over time, practice leads to mastery.

We have a practice —and the response to the practice. We continue to monitor results. We are feedback-aware. This is learning in action. It is as far away from ivory-tower theory and abstract knowledge acquisition as you can get. Learning is doing and responding.

What sort of feedback are you getting? What needs tweaking? What new possibilities surface now? What is your intuition telling you? How do you feel? At this point we have shifted again.

6. INTEGRATION

"My kid could do that!"

"What's it supposed to be?"

We're in the art museum. Impressionist painters are popular. Today, few people will be outraged by the landscape paintings of Monet or Cézanne. These artists' paintings have been reproduced millions of times the world over. Any Impressionist exhibition draws huge crowds. But it was not always so. In the late 1800s Impressionist paintings were seen as barbaric. The art-appreciating public couldn't get their minds around why anyone would want to daub canvasses in such a seemingly haphazard fashion. Surely this wasn't art. The standards of the day called for precise, realistic academic paintings. Impressionists were the bad boys (and girls) of the art world.

If a system is not prepared to absorb the new, it rejects it. Organ transplants fail. Hardware and software companies do rigorous compatibility testing. The mantra is "test early and test often." They take integration seriously. Simply trying to impose an idea on an existing system is asking for trouble.

Do you remember learning to drive a car? At first you needed a lot of focus. If you learned to drive with a stick shift it took a great deal of attention. You may have spent so long pressing the clutch and selecting the right gear that you had no excess capacity to actually look where you were going. At this level of skill you wouldn't last long let loose on the highway. But as you practiced, you got better. And in time these complexities became reflexes. Now they've become invisible to you. You formed a habit. That's a good thing because you need all your attention to see where you're going. You need to watch out for potential hazards. You need to find your destination. You integrated the mechanics of driving into your skill set. You expanded your attentional capabilities.

Initially, learning is a conscious act. Then it becomes automatic. You didn't learn to read in an afternoon. If you're going to learn a new accounting package, a new language, or to dance the tango, you need to take one small step at a time. With regular practice we master the new skills, and attention is freed up for what's next. Our brain offloads mastered techniques from the frontal cortex to subcortical structures and they become unconscious reflexes. Anatomically, we have grown dendrite. Our brains have created strong inter-connections in response to learning.

The result of practice is change in the whole system. That system could be a workplace, a team, a product line, a service, or select practice we master the a memetic structure (we'll have more to say about this in the next chapter). The incoming behavior may cause old ideas to die, or it may include and improve upon an existing idea. The newly integrated whole expands our range of responses. Over time, our integrated behavior becomes less visible and becomes the "new normal." Now the whole system is affected and is more capable. Again, another shift has occurred. Ideally the company or the team becomes more flexible and open to learning and adapting to fresh perspectives and different ways of being. Our businesses and personal responses shift toward becoming more adaptive, agile, and resilient.

THE NEXT SHIFT

The whole system now has moved from the initial entry point. New aspirations and challenges surface, and the process repeats. Small shifts are acknowledged and celebrated. Even a tiny change can have a big impact, as anyone would tell you who's had a mosquito in the bedroom. We continue to learn and grow. We notice what happened. What we pay attention to changes. We reevaluate our expectations, desires, and capabilities in the light of a revitalized energy and a better vantage point. And so we move our rock toward a destination.

The shifting process is flexible. There will be overlap at times. Innovative ideas can emerge from practice. We are always seeking to clarify the current situation. Identifying the kind of conversation we are having can help us locate where we are. What are we trying to do? What are we doing? Are we trying to describe a problem? Are we exploring further possibilities? Are we hoping to understand the consequences of putting our newly-formed idea into action? Will it play nicely within the current environment? Are we becoming more agile and resilient? Are we now better positioned to face the next challenge? What are the fruits of our courageous actions? What do we need to focus on next? Answer: "Chapter Four, Collaborative futures": desert journeys, memes, metronomes, fish, and rock bands.

CHAPTER FOUR

Collaborative Futures

n case you skipped the introduction, memes (rhymes with genes) are ideas that replicate themselves. If you've ever heard a song that you can't get out of your head, you've been "infected" by a meme. Memes mimic. They show up in multiple ways from fashion to business jargon. Memes are unexamined ideas that are simply copied.

You've probably walked into a hotel bathroom and seen the toilet paper end folded into an inverted "v". You don't do this at home, do you? No. But this little toilet-paper-origami trick is seen around the world from Boston to Bangalore. It has no purpose. It's a meme.

In his book *Virus of the Mind*, former Microsoft chairman Richard Brodie writes of how memes serve to create and limit the way we see the world. One example of memetic programming is peer pressure. We are influenced by those around us.

Memes make up the "value landscape" of individuals and groups. When individuals participate in a group they bring with them the values that drive their understanding, perspectives, and decision-making. We make choices based on our values. But where do we get those values? We are socially conditioned to recognize what is or isn't meaningful. It is those ideas, prohibitions, and aspirations that form memetic boundaries.

BOUNDARIES

Groucho Marx once quipped, "I wouldn't want to belong to any club that would have me as a member." When you join a club or a team you change your identity. You become a member. Your behavior is limited to what is acceptable by the group. We humans are social animals. We clump together into tribes, nations, families, user groups, companies, softball leagues, knitting circles, work teams and so on. Some group memberships are voluntary and others mandatory. It may be difficult to avoid being in the tax payers group, but for other affiliations we tend to congregate with those people who share our motivating perspectives.

A significant barrier to collaboration is the way we have been socially conditioned for individual achievement. Of course none of us would derive much value without individual achievement, but there is a dark side to this coin. What works well in one context can work against us in another.

Repetitious conversations signal we have reached a boundary limit. It's no good just doing more of the same only faster in the hope of reaching escape velocity. The old way doesn't fit the current reality, and the new paradigm has not yet come into being.

Imagine you are a doctor in the 1950s. By today's standards, surgery options are limited. There is no way you can realistically imagine the medical technology of today where we grow certain human organs in the laboratory. Our behavior and aspirations are limited by the ideas available to us.

So let's look at some common memetic structures. Think of these as developmental stages in which groups operate.

1. POWER

Two thousand years ago, the Greek general Thucydides said it best: "The strong do what they will and the weak suffer what they must." At its most basic level the strong exploit the weak. You are either with us or against us. Leaders operate through domination and control by the threat of serious consequences. Power engenders fear and compliance. It can be the stuff of empire building, wheeling and dealing. Do whatever it takes. Take no prisoners (and try to stay out of jail). The power meme will not be limited. It actively seeks to impose its own rules and regulations like that of an invading army, or a corporate raider. It will destroy what it sees as opposition. The power meme is dominant in street gangs and corporate boardrooms. However, more sophisticated power structures lead through influence and principled behaviors. The power meme seeks control, action, and expansion.

2. AVOIDANCE

This memetic structure is in opposition to the power meme. The avoidance meme limits power by creating rigid boundaries. All actions must be "by the book." Anything new will be rejected unless it is authorized. This meme dominates in bureaucracies and hierarchical organizations. Predictability, reliability, and compliance are highly prized. Creativity is shunned in the place of efficiency and duty. The ideas circulating in this memetic environment are intolerant of any deviance. The belief is that following the rules guarantees safety. The avoidance meme creates a culture of dependency. It sounds like this: "I'm not sticking my neck out."

3. ACHIEVEMENT

The avoidance meme drives the achievement meme crazy. This should sound familiar. It was how most of us were raised. This is where Sisyphus lives, too. The emphasis here is on an individual and action-oriented achievement. Risk-taking is embraced. Competitiveness and innovation are valued. The focus is on individualistic innovative future success. There is acknowledgment of the need to collaborate with others, but not at the expense of individual recognition. Moreover, collaborating with others is seen as weakening one's own status. This meme wants proof of achievement. It wants concrete results.

Individualism is status conscious. For example, academic institutions get their funding based on star-quality researchers. It is not uncommon for such experts to be unaware of similar research going on just down the hall.

Without looking at how individual achievement can get in the way of group cohesion, we will never successfully achieve collaboration. We can talk all we like about the need for collaboration, but in times of stress and chaos individual recognition and accomplishment will be the default positions unless we have the gumption to look at the problem squarely.

At one end, the boundary of the achievement meme bumps up against the avoidance meme. At the other end, the achievement meme is unwilling to let go long enough to expand its capabilities by becoming collaborative. No amount of happy talk about people magically getting along and sharing will take the place of well-designed structures that align individual and group incentives.

4. COLLABORATIVE

Prima donnas need not apply. The collaborative group forms a holistic organism. The focus here is to support the structure and its purpose. Each member contributes to the agility, resilience, experience, and effectiveness of the whole. This memetic organization values interpersonal connection. It's worth repeating here that this memetic structure is not management by consensus. The collaborative memetic community throws up a boundary against detrimental individualism. Capabilities are expanded. There is space for all voices to be heard as a prelude to decision-making. The group values synergy, contribution, mutual respect, diverse capabilities, and group purpose.

THE MEMBRANE

Think of a membrane around each of these structures, like a cell wall. The boundaries between these memetic structures harden when threatened. The automatic defense mechanism is for each side to state their values more adamantly, which does no good because each side has its fingers in its ears. Recognizing the values driving behavior is the first order of business. Only then can you start work on making the boundaries more porous and flexible. Small shifts in perception and behavior allow for positive movement.

MATCHING MEMES

The four memetic structures presented here are not types of people. A single person can operate from numerous perspectives depending on context. There may be times when a person must follow procedure (AVOIDANCE): for example, to comply with a legal requirement. At other times the same person, motivated to get things done (ACHIEVEMENT), may actively seek to circumvent unnecessary rigid compliance. The point here is that in any group, perspectives, and therefore motivations, will vary.

At any one time memes can be strong or weak. The tricky thing about memes is that they are hidden, and bringing them to light is disruptive. And of course this is where the courage comes in. Nevertheless, understanding what's going on from a memetic perspective gives us an entry point for more appropriate conversations leading to better behaviors.

Gridlock happens when groups are pulling in different directions. You need a resource-depleting state of inertia like a giraffe needs a TV set. Today, the most obvious example of conflicting value memes is in our highly-polarized national party politics.

One of two things is likely to happen if there is not a "memetic match." Either the individual will be rejected by the group, or the group will change. The other scenario is that the organization will take to its sickbed for a very long time.

Conflicting values are inherent in the workplace. At the other end of the spectrum we have "groupthink," mindless agreement. In fact, an attribute of all groups is some level of conformity which identifies members from non-members.

BIRDS OF A FEATHER...

Flocks of birds, schools of fish, and swarms of insects act in harmony. They group together for protection and scatter under predatory attack. No leader has to choreograph the beautiful shapes the creatures form. Naturalists have discovered that each creature is only aware of its local neighbors. A bird responds to flight, speed, and direction of other birds in its immediate surroundings. Birds tend to keep about three body lengths away from their neighbors. This space is enough to allow them to maneuver and at the same time monitor immediate behavioral changes. In this way the whole flock acts like a single entity. This is called synchronicity.

Here is an even stranger example of synchronicity. Once a metronome is set, its purpose is to keep its rhythm regardless of its surroundings. However, something remarkable happens when a group of metronomes are placed next to each other: they begin to synchronize. The metronome is a mechanical device. So how come it's aware of its environment and can change? Clearly, the metronome doesn't have a mind. It doesn't have emotions. Yet it exhibits group behavior. We won't go into the physics of how this happens here. However, each metronome is causing an effect on its local environment.

Think about collaboration as magnetic attraction.

IT ONLY TAKES TWO TO COLLABORATE

The Rolling Stones are unlikely subjects for study in business school, but the Jagger-Richards collaborative team has survived for 50 years. Successful collaboration takes place across a wide spectrum of business and creative activity.

Lennon and McCartney were about as successful as you can get. The founders of Home Depot, Arthur Blank and Bernie Marcus, were known as BernieArthur. What were these people doing right? Clearly, each of these successful people had a strong ego. Nevertheless, their egos didn't get in the way of the collaborative purpose. They demonstrated maturity and flexibility to balance self-interest, with the health and sustainability of the organization they cultivated.

The minimum requirement for a team is two people. As a team gains more members and grows in complexity, it needs more sophisticated leadership. Most business literature is focused on heroic solo-leaders or team building. Only now is more attention being paid to successful partnership. According to some sources dysfunctional partnerships are rife in high-tech industries. Nevertheless, Hewlett and Packard's partnership is legendary. Bill Gates relied on a number of partners while he was at Microsoft.

President Theodore Roosevelt said: "[T]he most important single ingredient in the formula of success is knowing how to get along with people." And what better way to start than by demonstrating some curiosity.

THE CAT KILLER

They say curiosity killed the cat. But this creature has nine lives—and you only have one. Being curious is unlikely to kill you, and it can do you a lot of good. If you're going to understand other people's worldviews, be curious. Of course, you need to respect personal privacy. Think about the last time someone was genuinely interested in what you had to say. It probably gave you that warm fuzzy feeling. Nevertheless, curiosity is no manipulative technique. We need to be curious about how our partners see the world, what they value, and what we have in common. Now this is no idle curiosity. It has direction. It seeks clarity.

There's a Gary Larson cartoon showing a person talking to a dog in one panel and the same person talking to a cat in the other. In the latter panel there is a cartoon balloon showing what the cat is thinking: it's blank. When you speak to other people, *you* know what you mean, but do they understand? Have you skipped over necessary explanations? Have you asked for feedback? Or, are you deluded in the imagining that what you say is what they hear? Were you curious about what *they* understood?

A surprising number of employees have no idea what the company they work for is trying to achieve. No one ever thought it was important to fill them in. No one ever joined up the dots for them between the employee's need for security and the well-being of the organization. Many employees see the workplace as nothing more than a trade—time for a paycheck. Beyond that they have about as much interest in the direction of the company as a baboon has in opening a checking account. Why should they? If no one has invited them to join in the right conversations, how can they feel included? The alienated worker is only left with his self-interest, and that may not be in alignment with company objectives. When we don't create and communicate a clear vision, our team members are left with unspoken assumptions. They will make up their own stories—and that might not be your story.

SADDLE UP THE CAMELS

In Paul Coelho's allegorical story, *The Alchemist*, the author describes a camel train crossing the desert. The harsh conditions cause difficulties for the travellers. At times they have to make detours to keep their animals from sinking into the soft sand. In other places the camels refuse to cross dried salt lakes. Boulders cause the group to make a temporary change of direction. Camel drivers become sick and unable to lead; they are replaced by others. Despite these temporary setbacks the travellers understand their overall direction. And while the journey is in progress their destination remains an imagined future: a vision.

FUZZY INTENTION

You may not be about to saddle up your camel, join the caravan, and set out across the dunes, but you do have an idea of a future—a vision—that doesn't yet exist. Intention is a general direction.

Have you ever had one of those moments where you forgot what you're about to say? Your intention was derailed by an unexpected mental connection—another thought intervened. Maybe the idea that surfaced has value. And that thought triggered other thoughts.

You momentarily lost the thread of where you were going. But sometimes we need to go in the what-looks-like-wrong short-term direction to get onto the right track. Imagine you're in your car and you want to go north. The freeway ramp heads south before it loops around to the north. If you insist on being right at every moment, you'd never allow yourself to take advantage of the freeway.

Intention is fuzzy. It is an imprecise path and allows for a flexible approach. Intention points to where we want to go.

SYNERGY

Storms will continue to pound the business terrain. But together we can create a resilient and flexible organization that bends with the prevailing winds. In better weather we shall actively flourish. Our guiding principle is intention. It helps us in the face of obstacles and temporary setbacks.

Inter-personal connection is the foundation of group effectiveness. Without the ability to tolerate criticism we shall be blind to real circumstance in a business climate that no one person can fully know. We need each other.

Tenacity is a valuable trait. But not the absolute, mindless vice-like grip of a Rottweiler. There are times when we must let go. A collaborative group will need to constantly survey the landscape and re-examine its assumptions in the light of ever-changing circumstances. We have to make difficult decisions. We must develop an awareness of what is ending before we can see clearly what is preventing our progress. Discarding what we no longer need is the courage to act. And courage comes through confronting difficulty. All of us struggle at times. It is only human to do so, but the collaborative leader is no wimp. Unlike condemned Sisyphus, struggling up his hill all alone, we have more options. A small shift in our perspective can open up brighter prospects.

The organization that values curiosity reaches beyond itself. Our intention is to hold our collaborative vision of a better future. Alone we can only hope for limited success: together we shall discover profitable and more satisfying futures.

A Life of Learning

My parents wanted the best for me. At least they wanted to know that their investment in my education would lead to getting a job. I followed their lead, and graduated from school with a degree in accounting (later completing my MBA in international finance.) But deep down, I always knew that I wouldn't be an accountant. I knew two things: I wanted my life to have meaning, and I wanted to do my own thing. I was never one to follow the rules. I felt rules restricted my creativity. I even interviewed for accounting jobs, but my heart wasn't in it. However, accounting gave me insight into the world of finance.

My curiosity led me into international banking. I love to travel, and I got to see the world. I spent a lot of time in South America, in Europe, and around the United States. I traveled continuously.

At an early stage in my career, I started to gain a deep understanding of risk. I was given a significant amount of responsibility in the early 1980s. At that time, there was no logic to the amount of risk the banks were giving to a young twenty-something like me. At 24, I was responsible for $3 billion in lines of credit. I was a loan officer working for a French bank and lending to global trading companies.

Today, my understanding of risk continues to serve me well. I'm able to help clients look at the entire life-balance sheet. Typically, I hear complaints: I can't afford to do that without making more money. This is a typical example of decision-making. I like to dig deeper and ask if that really is the case. Perhaps they have $5,000,000 in the bank and they are worried about reduced profits of 5 percent this year. When clients can't take out the $500,000 they're used to taking out, I wonder what world they're operating in. These are champagne problems.

Other clients may have huge amounts of credit card debt. They could be paying 22 percent interest. I find out they have $500,000 worth of unused equity in their home, and $150,000 of debt in their business that they personally guarantee. But they don't want to have the conversation with their spouse to say "Honey, we can take a 6 percent mortgage and pay off all our debts. This is better than paying 22 percent interest, which we'll be paying forever."

Back in the 1980s, I could see from my vantage point in banking that the world was changing. Although the bank was financially rewarding for me, I wanted to create something of my own. I walked into the office of the general manager and said: "I quit. I'm going to start my own business." He asked me what I was going to do. I said I didn't know. I had to end something to allow space for something new to emerge. I now embarked upon a new journey of self-discovery.

THE SEARCH

For three months during 1985, I traveled the length and breadth of Vermont. My prospective business partner, Chet, and I were looking for opportunities. We had decided upon food: jellies, jams, mustard, salad dressing, chocolate. We wanted to take one of these products and make it a regional or even national brand. Chet had a marketing background. We went to the Chamber of Commerce and identified 350 cottage industries. We knocked on every door of each business we found. Eventually, I learned that Chet and I were not natural collaborators. We displayed the classic Sisyphean problem: both of us wanted control. However, all of this was a necessary and valuable experience for my own evolutionary development as an entrepreneur. We decided to go our separate ways.

Ultimately, I ended up opening a chocolate business back in New Jersey. I love to see satisfied clients, and I, too, was a chocoholic. I still am. It was an easy business to get into. I didn't need a lot of culinary expertise. The product had a great shelf life. It was something I could be passionate about. And people got great pleasure from it. However, my search for freedom resulted in working seventeen hours a day for almost three years. This was a terrific learning experience. I found out what it took to run a small business: the importance of customer service, running production, and a host of retail issues.

THE TRADING FLOOR

I had no intention of becoming a commodity trader. My brother, Harold, was in the business. He was so busy he needed all the help he could get. While I was trying to sell my chocolate business, I went down onto the trading floor to lend a hand. My first reaction was: I could never do this. It's crazy! But then I started doing his daily profit and loss statements. I was astonished at just how much money a person can make trading commodities. Not only that, the cost of the trading seat at the time was very cheap. He trained me so I could trade on my own account.

Later, I partnered with a few other traders, and in the early 1990s I opened Odyssey Trading, along with my partner, John Lloyd. Collaborating gave us more leverage, and we hired trading assistants. We did well. We made money. But this all came at a price.

I worked in 4 World Trade Center in Manhattan. The environment was toxic. I was in a room with thousands of people. I worked in the sugar options ring at the Coffee, Sugar, and Cocoa Exchange. At peak, there were probably 150 people in my ring. We were jammed in there like commuters in a subway car during rush hour, pen marks all over our bodies. We had to wear special jackets to protect our clothes. The noise was deafening. People would be screaming, flailing their arms around. We couldn't avoid spilling ink on other people as we wrote down our orders. This was all before the days of handheld electronic devices.

It was a hellish environment. There was no real human interaction. It was just about making money. When the bell rang at the beginning of the day, friends became enemies.

It was like hand-to-hand combat. Relationships were dys-functional. When the bell rang at the end of the day, there would be a pretense of friendship. Perhaps someone who just screwed me out of thousands of dollars now wanted to go out and have a beer with me. For me, it was all in-authentic and unethical. You could only be honest to an extent with people. There was no room for growth. It was more about how much risk you were willing to take. How much were you willing to lose to risk making ten times more?

I felt trapped. But there were benefits. I got to see my kids grow up. I got home early. I made money. I tried to balance my life by sitting on not-for-profit boards. I engaged in a variety of charitable activities. I was hungry for personal freedom and greater purpose. But no one in my business environment talked about such things. My stress level became overwhelming. I realized that I needed to get out.

COLD TURKEY

The day came when I'd had enough. I remember it well. It was a pivotal moment. I was driving at the time. I called my wife and told her I was never going back to the trading floor. I said I had two choices: I'm either going to drive my car into the barrier or I'm going do something else. Either way, I wasn't going back to the trading floor. And I didn't go back. There was a brief period of transition where John Lloyd and my brother helped me get out of my positions.

The next big moment for me came not long after I left the trading floor. I had the idea I could use my financial skills away from the trading floor. But I hadn't formed my idea yet. This was fine, because I knew I could tolerate ambiguity. I didn't need to have all the answers. I met a gentleman, Mr. Miller, through my brother Larry. He was the CEO of a big financial institution. He suggested I speak to someone in his HR department who could help me get clarity around what I wanted to do next. I had no idea what I really wanted. I was curious.

GAINING CLARITY

Mr. Miller recommended that I speak to Gladys Chen. Gladys said there were two people who she would talk to when she was making a significant career decision. One is Marsha Hoch, who remains my business coach today. The other is Mary Burton, who was a career transition counselor at the time. It took me a couple of months during that spring of 1999 to find these two women. I hired Mary.

She took me through a three-month process. She helped me get clarity about what my passions and strengths were. Mary helped me uncover my core values and skills as a listener, a facilitator, and my intuitive abilities.

This was new territory for me. Core values! I was a commodity trader. What the hell is that? But this is the response I get from my clients all the time. I understand this reaction to values work. I realized that my stress was not about always making or losing money. My stress had to do with violating every one of my core values: including loyalty and professional growth. At the same time, Marsha was helping me evaluate business opportunities.

Mary asked me a lot of questions. They were the kind of questions no one had previously asked me. The reason I hired two coaches was that Mary specialized in career transition. She co-wrote a book called *In Transition* and taught at Harvard business school for some time. She took me through exercises over a period of several months that led me to personal clarity. Marsha helped me with my own self-discovery. In the beginning, she was more of a life coach.

I started working with Mary first, and as I was in Mary's process, I began to engage with Marsha. So this was a developmental process. A small shift allowed me to see the next step I needed to take.

The unspoken agreement I had with Mary, which is also the agreement I have with my clients, was that she opened up her network to me. There were people who were willing to give half an hour or so of their time on occasion. So Mary helped me speak to a number of people, and through some investigation I met my former partner, Mitch Schlimer.

SOUNDBOARD EMERGES

SoundBoard came into being when I met Mitch in 2000. He was involved in creating CEO peer groups. He and his partners were looking to expand their business. I brought the peer groups into New Jersey. However, within six months I realized that the business model made no financial sense. I loved what we were doing, but there were limitations to what the business was trying to accomplish. The problem lay with the existing model.

At one point we had close to one hundred organizations in peer groups. I was bringing in the business. CEO roundtables inevitably deal with surface issues. But I wanted to go deeper. Once inside an organization we gained a much fuller and diverse perspective. For me there was not so much gratification in only knowing the CEO perspective. The only way we were going to make a successful business model work, and at the same time have more fulfillment, was to get an in-depth understanding of the dynamics from multiple perspectives. And that required a different approach.

Clients open to real change wanted to bring us into their organizations. The challenge was they wanted me. I had personal relations with them. I brought these leaders into the peer groups in the first place. I got to know them. My partners were more interested in clients paying their dues for annual membership. For me, a functional relationship was far more important. I want—and need—to see the effects of what I do. The type of people I attracted was not the same type of people that my partners attracted. This was a mismatch. I started changing the structure over the next two years. It changed so much that it became unrecognizable from what had preceded it. I started to go down a more satisfying and effective path toward in-depth business leadership guidance. However, the original partners had a different vision, and consequently they left. Mitch remained as my partner for a further two years, but all was not well.

MY SISYPHEAN ROCK

Mitch and I had very different points of view. Mitch saw the expense. I saw the investment. I was bringing people into the business. He was uneasy. I felt I was single-handedly carrying the rock up the hill and Mitch was on the other side pushing it back down again. He fought hard to hold on to what had worked in the past. Yet our situation was changing. We needed office space. We needed a place for off-site groups. The year was 2005; I realized I had to have a partner who could share my vision. Bearing the burden of manifesting my dream alone was exhausting. It was obvious we had to build a team, and to improve our model. We needed to invest in sales and better marketing.

The problem was our peer groups were left to execute on their own. They can be cognitively committed to goals and action plans, but without ongoing guidance, the results are usually lackluster.

It's important for me to work with the person with whom our client is having a difficult conversation. I wanted to foster and facilitate those conversations. I wanted to take their team off-site and have those strategy sessions. I wanted to have my team coach multiple people and allow them to get clarity around their complex responsibilities.

The lesson I now had to learn was painful. But if there was pain, there was also gain. Loyalty remains one of my core values, but I learned about limits. Loyalty is a virtue, but unconditional loyalty can get you into a lot of trouble.

I'd just finished a coaching session with Marsha that Monday morning. I'd been talking about my differences with Mitch. I explained about my loyalty to him, and that he had some medical issues. She wasn't buying it. She looked me straight in the eyes and said: "So what are you ready to do? Do you want to keep complaining or make a change? I've been hearing the same old story for months and it's getting really challenging to hear. I'm not sure you're ready to do anything!" This was so unlike Marsha. And she got up abruptly and left the room.

I sat there for a long time. I thought to myself: What am I going to do? I came to the conclusion that I needed to get away. I called the travel agent. My daughter, Jessica, was spending part of her junior year in Australia. My wife and I had planned to go there at the end of the semester in June for three weeks. I called Jessica in Australia. She asked me what was going on. I told her that I just needed to get away. I had some business decisions to work out. That Thursday I was on my way to Australia.

I needed comfort. I found a consolidator ticket vendor that allowed me to fly first class. Jessica was in school during the day, but at the weekend and nights we were together. Ten days later, I was on my way back home.

Mitch was in the hospital when I arrived. He'd hurt his back and was in traction. His family was there in the hospital room, but they left us together to talk. I told him it was over and I couldn't do this anymore.

A week later, he was out of the hospital. He wanted to work things out. I said: "No, I don't think you heard me, I've made a decision." He filed a lawsuit against me. From mid-May to October 2005, we were in a contentious lawsuit. I didn't want to go to court, even though I knew all the facts were in my favor. My lawyer advised me to settle, be done with it, and get on with my life. Eventually, I was able to hear him. Now I was free to move forward: another lesson learned.

THE PATH CLEARS

This experience gave me clarity. If I want to reduce stress in my life, I need to honor my values in everything I do. This is not to say I'm perfect. But when I realize I'm not being perfect, this is why I feel the way I feel. I want to bring that concept of values and vision to my clients. This remains the root of our work: values and vision.

I realized I needed to build a team. Robin Adwar joined SoundBoard in 2001. Her years of corporate human resource experience bring our clients the tools they need to create healthier organizational climates and greater clarity for their staffs. Her articulacy, coaching acument and listening skills keep our clients accountable and focused. She became my partner when Mitch left in 2005. The ever-optimistic Lauren Canning continues to demonstrate her faith in the organization since she joined us in 2003. She is an expert at client-service and drives our marketing engine. Mike Rosone came in 2005. He was a client for five years before he joined our team. Our clients love his energy and value his operational skills. He brings a much-needed sense of humor and gratitude to whatever he is doing. Since 2007, Diane Gray has kept our office running smoothly and makes sure all of our meetings go off as planned. Jonathan Hakakian's passion for entrepreneurship, strategic planning and project management completed our core team in 2010. We continue to be augmented by a number of external specialists. All of us are committed to life-long learning, collaboration, and values alignment.

The central questions we ask are: For the purpose of what? Who are we? What is the future we want to create? We want to help our clients understand where they are currently, and uncover more effective and satisfying futures.

In the last three or four years there has been a distinct evolution. We've done a lot of training, learned to be good coaches, facilitators, and developed our expertise in group dynamics.

SIGNIFICANCE

My goal is to learn something new every day. It's an investment in co-creation. I'm in the process of thinking about future initiatives. I have a great passion to help the next generation of entrepreneurial leaders. We recently created SoundBoard Ventures to support young entrepreneurs and we are on our way to creating an Angel Fund to seed these ventures. I've also been speaking at universities a bit more. There is no money in all that right now. This is a personal and philanthropic expression of my gratitude. Eventually, SoundBoard Consulting and my philanthropic initiatives will come together. This book is a small shift in that direction. For me, the future will encompass this accumulated learning and entrepreneurial knowledge. This is not just my learning but an ongoing evolving action and significance for those around me. My role is one of discovery. I am a catalyst for others to discover where they truly are, the baggage they're holding onto, and the possibilities of a new and better future.

APPRECIATION

Sisyphus may be condemned to toil alone, but we are able to collaborate. Apart from my appreciation for our core team, there are people I would like to acknowledge as being my mentors. In spite of the 30,000 hours of leadership entrepreneurial conversations, these mentors, coaches, and consultants have helped me create, shape, and fine tune my perspectives on leadership guidance and healthy and sustainable business growth.

My mentors have helped me evolve, and I feel a deep sense of gratitude toward them. All along the way, I've been lucky. I was lucky to find Gladys Chen who introduced me to Mary Burton and Marsha Hoch, both of whom I've mentioned above. Mary Burton taught me that transition is possible at any stage of our career and to pay attention to recurring themes in our lives. Marsha Hoch continues to help me stay aligned with my values, and not to spread myself too thin. She helped me realize that for me it's not about the money. It's about being valued and respected.

Kenneth Sole, Ph.D, a consultant and leadership trainer, was my mentor in New Hampshire. He taught me everything I know about group dynamics and conflict. From him, I learned the importance of creating a void for other people to fill. And as far as conflict is concerned, I learned the power of stretching tension and conflict to its outer limits, and thereby finding the true learning and growth. I particularly like to work with conflict resolution. However, without Ken, I would probably not have the same ability to take a facilitative approach which means to "allow". To let happen what happens.

I learned what it is to deepen the space between thinking and doing from author and consultant, Peter Senge, and the work of C. Otto Scharmer's *Theory U*. Both of these people made me aware of limiting assessments, the importance of allowing ourselves to see what is right in front of us, being present, and the impact of theory on strategic planning and creating new possibilities.

Jon Brandt is a client who recently sold his business for a considerable sum. He helped me see the value of taking a more strategic approach to marketing, and how to value a brand using content and information as an entry point. Jon taught me the concept of "pathing." Without my engagement with him, I wouldn't see niches in the same way.

Cal Calligaro and Scott Darling, both long-time clients and friends, elevated my ability to ask probing questions, think more strategically and more fully appreciate the value of my experiences.

Birgit Zacher Hanson and Susan Freeman are strategic partners in Florida. From them, I came to an understanding that most breakdowns are the result of missing conversations. They showed me the power of having the right conversation, and introduced me to the concept of an agreement/integrity loop. I am grateful to my strategic partner in Pennsylvania, Scott Blessing, who first introduced me to somatic work: the importance of the body in leadership. Strategic partners Christiane St. Amour in Montreal, and Jay Wolf in New York, partners in JCris Consulting, taught me much about how organizational climate has an impact on productivity.

Several authors have been immensely influential. Pat Lencioni's *Five Dysfunctions of a Team* has been a valuable research tool in terms of team development and the effectiveness of storytelling. Charles Fletman's *The Thin Book of Trust* further developed my understanding of the importance of transparency and vulnerability. Reading Jim Collins's first book, *Built to Last*, helped me fully understand and appreciate staying in alignment with one's core values. Everything else can be adjusted to fit the market opportunities, such as competition and changing economic environments. Michael Gerber's book, *The E Myth*, led me to understand distinctions between entrepreneur, manager, and technician. Gerber writes that most businesses are started by technicians who had an "entrepreneurial seizure" and that they begin systematizing the business from day one in order to make it repeatable. And I don't want to leave out the value of that classic and influential author, Napoleon Hill, and his classic book, *Think and Grow Rich*.

I want to acknowledge my wife Carol-Ann and two grown-up daughters, Jessica and Risa, who have stood by my side throughout this amazing journey, never questioning my intentions.

I most appreciate my parents who gave me their unconditional support and taught me that life is about learning, and to focus not on the problems, but on the solutions. Without them, this book would not exist.

 Richard Magid, a recognized expert in leadership coaching and development, founded SoundBoard Consulting Group in 2000 to support business leaders in building more productive and profitable companies through the ideals of collaborative leadership. With more than 30,000 hours of coaching experience, Richard is trained in Advanced Facilitation, Conflict Resolution, and Executive Coaching. His strategic insights come from starting three companies and consulting with over 250 businesses in the past 30 years. Richard earned a bachelor's degree in accounting and a master's in international finance from New York University.

Contact Info:

Richard Magid, President
SoundBoard Consulting Group, LLC
6 Mars Court, Boonton Township, NJ 07005
Phone: 973-334-6222 x102
Richard@soundboardconsulting.com

My Golden Retriever

PUT YOUR PUPPY'S FIRST PICTURE HERE

Dog's Name _____

Date _____ Photographer _____

Physical Characteristics
of the Golden Retriever
(from the American Kennel Club's breed standard)

Color: Rich, lustrous golden of various shades. Feathering may be lighter than rest of coat.

Back line: Strong and level from withers to slightly sloping croup.

Tail: Well set on, thick and muscular at the base, following the natural line of the croup.

Hindquarters: Broad and strongly muscled. Legs straight when viewed from rear.

Size: Males 23–24 inches in height at withers; females 21.5–22.5 inches. Weight for dogs 65–75 pounds; bitches 55–65 pounds.

Coat: Dense and water repellent with good undercoat. Outer coat firm and resilient, neither coarse nor silky, lying close to body; may be straight or wavy.

Feet: Medium size, round, compact and well knuckled, with thick pads.

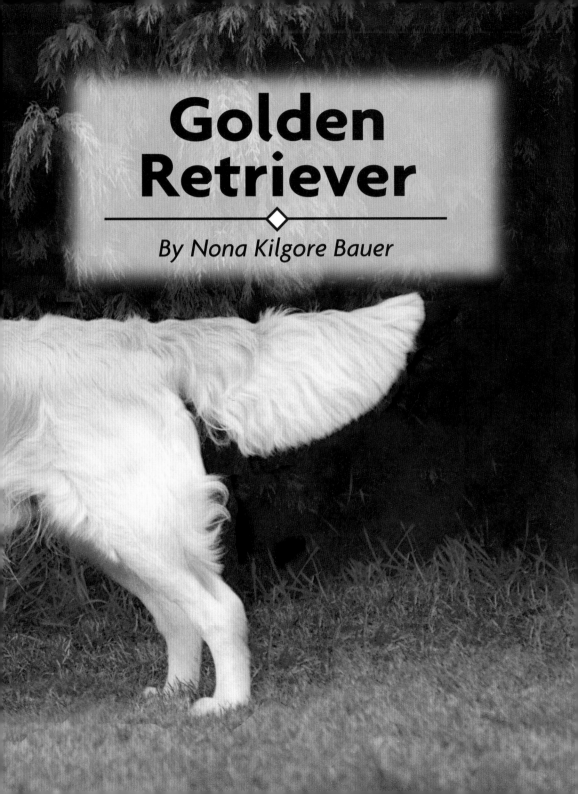

Golden Retriever

By Nona Kilgore Bauer

9

History of the Golden Retriever

Trace the ancestry of the youngest of the retriever breeds to its foundation dogs; meet the creator of the breed, an avid sportsman and hunter; and learn about the original purpose and talents of this most beautiful of gun dogs.

19

Characteristics of the Golden Retriever

Find out if the Golden Retriever is the ideal dog for you and your lifestyle. Consider the breed's size, required coat care and time and exercise needs, as well as the temperament and aptitudes of this active and affectionate sporting dog.

27

Breed Standard for the Golden Retriever

Learn the requirements of a well-bred Golden Retriever by studying the description of the breed set forth in the American Kennel Club standard. Both show dogs and pets must possess key characteristics as outlined in the breed standard.

31

Your Puppy Golden Retriever

Be advised about choosing a reputable breeder and selecting a healthy, typical puppy. Understand the responsibilities of ownership, including home preparation, acclimatization, the vet and prevention of common puppy problems.

59

Everyday Care of Your Golden Retriever

Enter into a sensible discussion of dietary and feeding considerations, exercise, grooming, traveling and identification of your dog. This chapter discusses Golden Retriever care for all stages of development.

79

Training Your Golden Retriever

by Charlotte Schwartz
Be informed about the importance of training your Golden Retriever from the basics of housebreaking and understanding the development of a young dog to executing obedience commands (sit, stay, down, etc.).

Contents

KENNEL CLUB BOOKS® **GOLDEN RETRIEVER**
ISBN: 1-59378-212-8

Copyright © 2003, **2007** • Kennel Club Books® • A Division of BowTie, Inc.
40 Main Street, Freehold, NJ 07728 USA
Cover Design Patented: US 6,435,559 B2 • Printed in South Korea

Photography by:
Norvia Behling, Carolina Biological Supply, Liza Clancy, David Dalton, Kent and Donna Dannen, Doskocil, Isabelle Français, Gold-Rush Kennels, Bill Jonas, James Hayden-Yoav, James R. Hayden, RBP, Carol Ann Johnson, Dwight R. Kuhn, Dr. Dennis Kunkel, Alice Pantfoeder, Mikki Pet Products, Antonio Philippe, Phototake, Jean Claude Revy, Nikki Sussman, Karen Taylor, Alice van Kempen and C. James Webb.

Illustrations by Renée Low.

Thanks to *The Seeing Eye®*, Morristown, NJ.

The Golden Retriever is the most beautiful and talented of the retriever breeds. It was originally developed to retrieve birds shot down over water. Dogs are trained, as shown here, with a dummy.

HISTORY OF THE

GOLDEN RETRIEVER

The youngest and most beautiful of the retriever breeds, the Golden Retriever was originally developed as a waterfowl dog. Although still an admirable shooting dog, the Golden today spends more time romping with the family than in the duck blind or the field. Often considered the ideal dog to hunt over, compete with or just live with and hug a lot, the Golden has something to offer the sportsman, dog fancier or professional dog lover.

The Golden Retriever can trace its ancestry back to a single breeding and the first pair of yellow retrievers destined to be called "Golden." The fancy is indebted to a Scotsman, the former Sir Dudley Marjoriebanks, first Lord Tweedmouth of Guisachan at Inverness, Scotland, and the first "breeder" of our golden dog.

Typical of 19th-century aristocracy, Tweedmouth was an avid sportsman and waterfowl enthusiast. His passion as a hunter was equaled only by his dedication to the sporting dog, having owned and bred Beagles, pointers, setters, Greyhounds, Scottish Deerhounds and Irish Water Spaniels.

During the 1850s he turned his attention to the moderate-sized retriever varieties who were the "water dogs" of that era. Such dogs were known to be desirable combinations of setters and spaniels and other working varieties. They possessed great courage, strength, sagacity and temperament, and, not surprisingly, a superior nose. Although color was unimportant to most sportsmen, who understandably cared more about working capabilities, Tweedmouth was a true vanguard of his time and was

The color of the Golden Retriever is any shade of rich, lustrous golden. They are powerful for their size and highly intelligent.

bent on developing a yellow retriever strain.

For many years the dog fancy embraced the romantic myth that Tweedmouth had acquired his first yellow dogs from a troupe of Russian circus dogs. That "golden" tale was dispelled by the late Elma Stonex of Somerset, England, the recognized judge and breeder of the Dorcas Goldens, a noted authority on Golden Retrievers who researched and uncovered the true history of the breed.

In an article in *Dog World* magazine, Mrs. Stonex wrote of information published in 1952 and 1953 in *Country Life* magazine. Contributed by the sixth Earl of Ilchester, a noted historian and sportsman, the articles revealed the breeding records of his great-uncle, Lord Tweedmouth, from his kennel at his Guisachan estate.

Those records, dated 1835 through 1890, contain no reference to dogs of Russian origin. They indicated that Tweedmouth purchased his first yellow retriever in Brighton in 1865, a dog named Nous (the Greek word for wisdom) out of a litter of otherwise all-black Wavy-Coated Retrievers.

Recorded as bred by the Earl of Chichester, Nous is shown in photographs from 1870 to be a large and handsome dog with a very wavy medium-color coat, very much resembling the modern Golden Retriever.

Two years later, Tweedmouth's cousin, David Robertson, presented him with a Tweed Water Spaniel named Belle. David lived at

Golden Retrievers were developed as outdoor dogs. They were regarded as companions for the lonely hunter, assistants to bring in downed game, and handsome working animals. To this day Goldens enjoy outdoor activities more than anything.

Even though Golden Retrievers are large dogs, heavily boned and muscled, they can maneuver gracefully, hunt for long hours in the field and run at a rapid, sustained pace.

Ladykirk, which was located on the Tweed River, and the Tweed Water Spaniel was the preferred hunting dog of that region. Historians describe the Tweed Water Spaniel as "a small English Retriever of a liver color" (liver meaning all shades of sandy, fawn or brown), a dog with a tightly curled coat who was an apparent descendant of the composite "Water Dogs" of the early nineteenth century. Belle was destined to become the foundation of Tweedmouth's plan to develop a yellow retriever breed.

In 1868 the now-famed breeding of Nous and Belle resulted in four yellow pups that Tweedmouth named Ada, Cowslip, Crocus and Primrose. He kept Cowslip to continue his pursuit of breeding yellow retrievers, and gave the other three pups to relatives and friends who shared his dream of producing superior yellow dogs. Ada was given to his nephew, the fifth Earl of Ilchester, who founded the Melbury line of retrievers and often crossed his yellow progeny with other Wavy-Coats and Labradors.

GOLDEN VIRTUES

Early writers spoke of the virtues of the Water Spaniel, ancestor of the Golden Retriever. "He rushes in with the most incredible fortitude and impetuosity, through and over every obstacle that can present itself, to the execution of his office... He rivals every other breed in his attachment to his master." Those same words easily describe the twenty-first-century Golden.

In 1873 Cowslip was bred to another Tweed Water Spaniel, also given by David Robertson, and Tweedmouth kept a bitch pup he named Topsy. Three years later Topsy produced Zoe, who was later bred twice to Sweep, a descendant of Ada and bred by Lord Ilchester. In 1884 Zoe whelped another litter, this time sired by Jack, another son of Cowslip, who had been sired by a red setter in 1876. This litter produced a second Nous, who is the final link between Tweedmouth's breedings and today's Golden Retriever.

This second Nous was bred to a dog named Queenie, who was out of Nous' sister and a black Flat-Coat sire. Two pups, Prim and Rose, no doubt named for their generations-removed ancestors, are believed to be behind the first two Golden Retrievers registered with The Kennel Club of Great Britain.

This last yellow litter from Nous and Queenie, recorded in 1889, shows four different lines

Golden Retrievers are often credited with having derived from the Tweed Water Spaniel. They possess a great love of water.

GENUS *CANIS*

Dogs and wolves are members of the genus *Canis*. Wolves are known scientifically as *Canis lupus* while dogs are known as *Canis domesticus*. Dogs and wolves are known to interbreed. The term canine derives from the Latin derived word *Canis*. The term "dog" has no scientific basis but has been used for thousands of years. The origin of the word "dog" has never been authoritatively ascertained.

going back to Cowslip in five generations. Linebreeding of this nature was most unusual in those days, so Tweedmouth was a true pioneer of his time.

Although reading about "Dogs A and B" bred to "Dogs C and D" and beyond can become somewhat tiresome, these important detailed records reveal how the Golden's yellow coat became the hallmark of the breed. The second Lord Tweedmouth followed his father's dream and bred yellow retrievers until Guisachan was sold in 1905, although sadly, he failed to keep records of his breedings.

A Golden Retriever, bringing to the hunter a downed pheasant. Goldens must have "soft mouths," which means they don't damage the game when they retrieve it.

The final connection between Tweedmouth's yellow retrievers and today's Golden pedigrees is contained in a letter to his daughter, Marjorie Lady Pentland, written by John MacLennan, one of the Guisachan keepers. MacLennan had a litter of pups from a daughter of Lady, a bitch owned by the Hon. Archie Marjoriebanks, Tweedmouth's youngest son. In his letter, MacLennan stated he had sold two pups to the first Viscount Harcourt, founder of the famous Culham Kennel, whose dogs are behind the entire Golden Retriever breed. Those two pups are believed to be descendants of Prim and Rose, and the foundation stock of the Culham line.

Lord Harcourt was a major player in those early Golden years and was the first exhibitor to show the breed in England (then known and registered as Flat-Coats, Golden) at the Crystal Palace show in 1908. His great sires, Culham Brass and Culham Copper (1905), were registered with The Kennel Club in 1903 and 1905.

In 1906 Lord Harcourt was joined in the ring by Winifred Maude Charlesworth, the most notable of early Golden aficionados. Mrs. Charlesworth spent 50 years breeding, training and campaigning her beloved Goldens. She was the force responsible for the formation of the Golden Retriever Club in 1913, and

During the early 20th century, the Golden Retriever was referred to as the Yellow Retriever. The term "yellow" was formally dropped in 1920 in favor of the current name.

for many years she served as Honorary Secretary for the Club. That same year, also largely due to Mrs. Charlesworth's efforts, Goldens were afforded their own category and registered as "Yellow or Golden Retrievers." The "Yellow" was officially dropped in 1920.

The importance of Mrs. Charlesworth to the Golden breed is legendary among Golden fanciers. Under the prefix of Normanby (later changed to Noranby), her breedings to Lord Harcourt's famous sires appear in every Golden Retriever pedigree today. She was a dynamic person-ality, and her dedication to the breed established the Golden as a premier gun dog in the British retriever world. Active in field trials as well as conformation, Mrs. Charlesworth was dedicated to the preservation of the working

BRAINS AND BRAWN
Since dogs have been inbred for centuries, their physical and mental characteristics are constantly being changed to suit man's desires for hunting, retrieving, scenting, guarding and warming their master's laps. During the past 150 years, dogs have been judged according to physical characteristics as well as functional abilities. Few breeds can boast a genuine balance between physique, working ability and temperament.

Golden who combined both type and soundness. Her dogs were sound and powerfully built, with lovely heads, and took honors on the bench and in the field. Her energy and enthusiasm in both venues promoted the Golden as a most capable gun dog who was competitive with the other retrievers of that time. In her 1933 book, she credits Lord Tweedmouth as instrumental in obtaining her first Golden, Normanby Beauty, which leads the reader to assume that bitch was directly from a Tweedmouth breeding.

In the early 1900s, retrievers of all colors competed in the field trial meets. In 1904 the

International Gundog League Open Stake was won by a "liver Flat-Coat" who was recorded as sired by Lord Tweedmouth's Golden Flat-Coat Lucifer, an accomplishment heralded by some historians as possibly the first Golden Retriever field trial win. The important fact remains that most Goldens of that era who competed on the bench also took honors in the field.

THE GOLDEN COMES TO THE USA

British immigrants brought Golden Retrievers with them to North America in the late 1800s, and Goldens from Britain and Canada were imported to the US during the 1920s. In 1925, the Golden Retriever was officially recognized

> ### BE A "SPORT"
> Yellow pups occasionally appear in litters of all-black retrievers. The color is due to a recessive gene. Such deviation from the normal pattern is considered a mutation, and the resulting yellow pup is called a "sport."

by the American Kennel Club (AKC) and by the Canadian Kennel Club in 1927.

American sportsman Colonel Samuel S. Magoffin founded the Golden Retriever Club of America (GRCA) in 1938 and acted as the club's first president. His hard-working hunting dog, Speedwell Pluto, became the breed's first AKC bench champion in 1930. Magoffin also takes credit for owning the

Whether you are considering a Golden Retriever as a pet, show dog, field worker or competition dog, the breed is among the most handsome of all pure-bred dogs.

One of the Golden Retriever's most admired characteristics is its water-repellent undercoat, which essentially keeps the skin dry, thus making the dog more buoyant.

second and third bench champions as well. The breed's first national specialty show and field trial took place in 1940 in Wisconsin. The conformation specialty was won by Beavertail Gail Lady. Both the show and the field trial were equally supported, and early Golden club members were dedicated to establishing a handsome, working retriever in the US. Today the emphasis in the States is clearly on conformation, and the national specialty usually has at least five times as many show dogs as field dogs entered. The club publishes a bi-monthly newsletter called the "Golden Retriever News." The GRCA, in an effort to promote the breed's natural hunting abilities, introduced special Working

Certificate Tests and, in an effort to promote the breed's prowess in conformation, obedience and field work, started the Versatility Certificate program. Both of these programs award titles as suffixes to the dog's name (WC, WCX, VC and VCX).

The Golden Retriever has enjoyed tremendous popularity in the US, beginning in the 1940s and continuing to this

CALL ME "HONEY"
In India, a six-year-old police-trained Golden Retriever named Madhu (the Indian word for honey) was used to guard the palace grounds and home of the late Prime Minister Nehru.

day. Only the Labrador Retriever outranks the Golden Retriever as the most popular sporting and pet dog in the country.

There are too many Golden Retriever breeders who have made American breed history to name them all. Some of the most influential kennels include: Gilnockie, Rockhaven, Stilrovin, Cragmount, Goldwood, Beautywood, Gunnerman, Tonkahof, Sprucewood, Cheyenne, Sun Dance, Golden Knoll, Malagold, Pepperhill, and many others. All these early kennels produced not only bench champions but also hard-working hunters. Goldens have left their mark not only on the conformation ring but, more impressively, on the obedience and field trial worlds. The first three Obedience Trial Champions, the highest possible title in AKC obedience competition, were Golden Retrievers. Likewise, there are many Field Champion Goldens as well, though few Dual Champions (earning both a Champion of Record in the show ring and a Field Champion title). Stilrovin Nitro Express became the breed's first Dual Champion, earning his

Golden Retriever puppies are very playful and mischievous. Few can resist the charms and antics of a pair of Golden pups. They usually mature mentally when they are about two years old.

Field Champion title in 1942 and his bench title in 1947. The last such Dual Champion was Tigathoes Funky Farquar, owned by Dottie Mikeska, who earned this title in 1979. In today's American Golden scene, there are few to no contenders for this elusive title of titles!

The Goldens in the 1930s claimed a few Best in Show awards; the first such winner was the breed's first bench champion, American and Canadian Ch. Speedwell Pluto (1933), followed by Ch. Toby of Willow Loch (1938). The first Golden to win Best in Show on more than one occasion was Ch. Dzar of Wildwood, who won six shows between 1946 and 1950. Many Best in Show Goldens have followed in these footsteps, and today Goldens are a popular choice for that highest of conformation wins.

Retrieving and swimming come as naturally to a Golden Retriever as being a devoted companion dog. Here a Golden Retriever fetches a downed duck.

CHARACTERISTICS OF THE
GOLDEN RETRIEVER

It might be *apropos* to call the Golden Retriever the "golden treasure at the rainbow's end." As the ideal all-around companion and sporting dog, the Golden offers something for every person or inclination. Tweedmouth's masterful linebreeding cemented the superb qualities of his yellow retrievers and, many generations later, Goldens remain the most versatile of the retriever breeds. Supremely intelligent and blessedly trainable, they also remain as devoted to their masters as the dogs of yore. Their talent is without equal, and the modern Golden excels in every canine discipline, including simple household amusements such as stick-fetch and shoe and sock theft. The Golden's disposition is as sunny as his outer coat, and he is considered by many to be the perfect family dog, the ideal companion for all ages and activities.

While the Golden Retriever may be the ideal dog, not every person is an ideal owner. You may love dogs and have a soft spot for the Golden, but love alone is not enough. Consider the big picture before you add a Golden to your household.

If you want to keep your Golden Retriever looking as beautiful as this dog, you must be prepared for the daily grooming and exercising of your pet.

SIZE

The Golden is a medium-to-large-sized dog who requires a good bit of space indoors and out. Everything about the dog is big, including his hairy paws, which will track mud and dirt onto your kitchen floor. His happy wagging tail will sweep your prized glassware from low-standing table tops. His natural curiosity will lead to rows of nose prints on the glass above your windowsills. Given a single opportunity, he will claim at least two couch cushions or your easychair. A fenced yard

or large-sized kennel run is a must to safely confine and exercise a large and energetic Golden Retriever.

Goldens thrive on fun activities with their owners. Few breeds demand as much time and energy from their owners as the Golden Retriever. This fellow is ready for more!

COAT AND COLOR

Part of the Golden Retriever's universal appeal is his lovely golden coat. Although a wide variety exists in length, texture and color, the golden coat is still his most distinguishing characteristic. Colors range from very pale cream to gold, but excludes dark red or mahogany shades. The lighter shades are more common in the show ring, with proponents of the darker golden passionately dedicated to their color preference. Most coats are straight to slightly wavy and of medium length, although longer coats also are more common on the bench. Coat color also has no bearing on intelligence, temperament or ability. Professional grooming is an option, but if you decide to use a grooming service, investigate the cost and be sure you can handle that expense.

TIME AND EXERCISE

The biddable personality of the Golden Retriever is no accident. His strong work ethic and desire to please were traits important to Lord Tweedmouth and were paramount in his yellow strain of dogs. As a gentle, friendly dog with a most forgiving disposition, the Golden wishes only to make his owner happy. He will not thrive in solitude and needs to live as part of his family unit.

Goldens are also natural athletes who are joyful workers and willing to try any sport or physical activity as long as there is a human at the other end. These are energetic dogs who require exercise and an active lifestyle to

"DOUBLE-COATED"

As if one coat isn't enough, the Golden is a "double-coated" breed, possessing an outer coat of long silky guard hairs and a soft downy undercoat that insulates the dog from temperature extremes, an important characteristic in a dog who must retrieve birds, especially waterfowl, under all weather conditions.

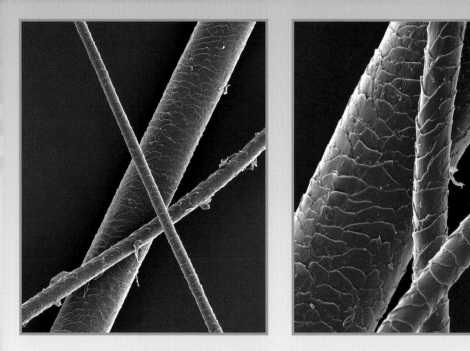

The two photos above show normal Golden Retriever hairs magnified 60–150 times their actual size.
The two lower photos show distressed hairs that are smashed (right) or frayed (left).

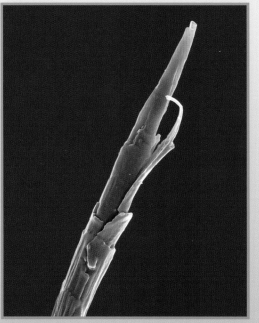

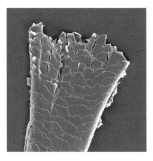

channel their enthusiasm in the right direction. A play area is not enough. Your Golden will not exercise without you. YOU are his reason to run, walk or play. You must commit to at least one good walk each day, plus daily games of fetch, Frisbee games or bumper chasing (those large canvas rolls sold in pet shops and pet-supply catalogs for retrieve-a-holic dogs). Daily exercise periods will keep your Golden physically fit and stimulated and too tired to entertain himself destructively. Exercise is also a natural canine (and human!) stress-reliever and will help prevent symptoms of separation anxiety and other stress-related behaviors from occurring.

Although most Goldens are energetic adolescents, some lines

> **THE HUNTER'S COAT**
> The Golden coat can create problems for the hunter, who must comb out seeds, burrs and tangled twigs after a long day in the field.

of show dogs produce more laid-back pups with lower energy requirements. If your canine companion goal is a Golden couch potato, research breeders who do not stress the working aspects of the breed. Be sure the puppy's parents are calm individuals both indoors and out; scrutinize their response to play activities. Check the breeder's references and past puppy owners to learn more about the temperaments of other pups. Good research should produce puppies you will enjoy living with.

Goldens can be highly trained as hunting dogs. They can be trained to respond to various whistle commands, in addition to hand signals and verbal commands.

DISCIPLINE

Even laid-back Golden Retriever puppies will require training to learn the rules of their new human world. Although highly trainable, Goldens are not born already trained, a surprise to some new owners who expect their Golden puppy to behave like the model Golden citizens they see on television. Good manners are not included in his purchase price. It is up to you to teach your Golden acceptable behavior in your home and in your neighborhood. That means weekly obedience classes with an experienced instructor and practice sessions with your Golden every day. If you cannot or will not commit to the time constraints of puppy training, perhaps you should rethink your decision to get this dog.

ORAL FIXATION

As a breed, Goldens are very oral dogs; after all, let us not forget their retrieving heritage. From pup to senior, most Goldens love, indeed they need, to have something in their mouths. It does not matter if that object is a toy, a table leg or your left hand. What is important is that this dog loves and needs to chew.

One of your major puppy challenges is teaching your puppy what he may or may not put between his tiny teeth. That will take effort, time and patience, but your pup is worth all that and more. Read the sections on techniques to discourage inappropriate chewing. If by four or five months of age, your pup still chews destructively, seek the help of a professional canine behaviorist. The dog may in fact be fine, and the problem might be you.

NOT A GUARD DOG

Given all the people-friendly qualities of the breed, it is no

This Golden puppy didn't know that digging up the yard is forbidden. Proactive training is a must with Golden puppies. Be certain your pup understands all the household rules.

"SNOW NOSE"

A Golden Retriever's nose may turn slightly pink during long periods of very cold weather. Called a "snow nose," the discoloration is normal and the nose will return to black when warm weather returns. The color of the nose leather sometimes fades in older dogs and may become pinkish-brown as the dog ages.

surprise most Goldens fail as guard dogs. The typical Golden might lick a home invader to death, which is not protection at its best. A Golden can be encouraged to give a warning bark, but his wildly wagging tail is a dead give-away.

However, despite their ingrained friendly attitude, stories abound about Goldens who have sensed danger to their families, especially their children, and reacted to protect them. While most Goldens owners believe their dogs would give up the family silver, they also trust that their dogs would rise to their personal defense.

THE GOLDEN'S NATURAL APTITUDES

OBEDIENCE AND AGILITY
As sporting dogs, Goldens are naturally athletic. They are also very trainable and obedient. Therefore, it is no surprise to see a large entry of Goldens in obedience competition and agility trials. Depending on how much advanced training you want to do with your Golden, these are areas in which the Golden excels and may be of interest to the Golden owner.

OTHER PURSUITS
The Golden Retriever has branched into many other areas

The ever-friendly Golden Retriever makes a far better guide dog and hunting dog than he could ever make a guard dog. This young pup has a bright future ahead of him.

beyond the show ring and field, all of which demonstrate the breed's unwavering devotion to humankind. The Golden has been used in every imaginable pursuit, including drug and arson detection, where the breed's super "sniffer" is put to great service; therapy work for nursing homes, children's hospitals and correctional facilities, where the Golden's sweet and steady temperament makes the dog ideal for sensitive interfacing with the elderly, the infirmed and the incarcerated; service work for the blind and the deaf, where the breed's superior intelligence and trainability, reliability and adaptability give the disabled companionship and assistance in their everyday lives; search-and-rescue work, where the breed's nose, persistence and work ethic enable the dog to

save lives. Goldens were among the breeds employed in the search-and-rescue efforts at the Oklahoma City bombing and the World Trade Center "Ground Zero" recovery project.

PHOTO COURTESY OF THE SEEING EYE®, MORRISTOWN, NJ

Golden Retrievers and their owners frequently participate in field trials. Goldens are naturally obedient, intelligent and very trainable.

Thousands of Goldens are trained as guide dogs for the visually impaired with dignity and devotion.

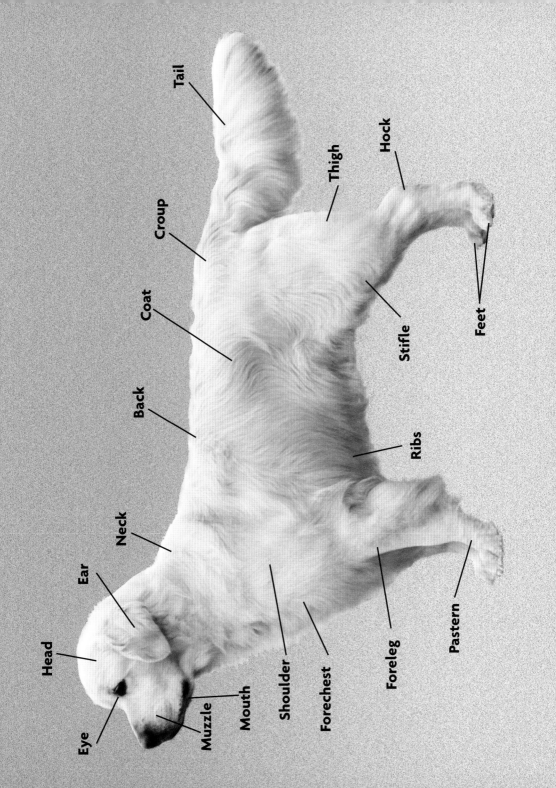

BREED STANDARD FOR THE

GOLDEN RETRIEVER

In order to appreciate, select and understand a proper Golden Retriever puppy or adult, it's important also to understand the American Kennel Club standard for the breed. Breed standards are the guidelines which have for decades preserved the qualities that define each breed of dog. Standards have been developed to protect and advance the soundness, temperament, natural ability and personality reflected in those qualities. Let us look at some of the key attributes of the Golden, as outlined in the following excerpts from the AKC's breed standard.

General Appearance: A symmetrical, powerful, active dog, sound and well put together, not clumsy nor long in the leg, displaying a kindly expression and possessing a personality that is eager, alert and self-confident. Primarily a hunting dog, he should be shown in hard working condition. Over-all appearance, balance, gait and purpose to be given more emphasis than any of his component parts.

Size, Proportion, Substance: Males 23–24 inches in height at withers;

females 21.5–22.5 inches. Weight for dogs 65–75 pounds; bitches 55–65 pounds.

Head: Broad in skull, slightly arched laterally and longitudinally without prominence of frontal bones (forehead) or occipital bones. Stop well defined but not abrupt. Foreface deep and wide, nearly as long as skull. Muzzle straight in profile, blending smoothly and strongly into skull.

The Golden's kind and intelligent nature shines through in his eyes and overall expression.

Eyes: Friendly and intelligent in expression. Color preferably dark brown.

Ears: Rather short with front edge attached well behind and just above the eye and falling close to cheek.

Nose: Black or brownish black.

Neck: Medium long, merging gradually into well laid back shoulders, giving sturdy, muscular appearance.

Back line: Strong and level from withers to slightly sloping croup, whether standing or moving.

Body: Well-balanced, short coupled, deep through the chest. Chest between forelegs at least as wide as a man's closed hand including thumb, with well developed forechest.

Tail: Well set on, thick and muscular at the base, following the natural line of the croup.

Forequarters: Muscular, well co-ordinated with hindquarters and capable of free movement. Legs, viewed from the front, straight with good bone, but not to the point of coarseness.

Feet: Medium size, round, compact and well knuckled, with thick pads. Excess hair may be trimmed to show natural size and contour. Splayed or hare feet to be faulted.

Hindquarters: Broad and strongly muscled. In a natural stance, the femur joins the pelvis at approximately a 90 degree angle; stifles well bent; hocks well let down with short, strong rear pasterns. Legs straight when viewed from rear.

Coat: Dense and water repellent with good undercoat. Outer coat firm and resilient, neither coarse nor silky, lying close to body; may be straight or wavy. Untrimmed natural ruff; moderate feathering on back of forelegs and on under-body; heavier feathering on front of neck, back of thighs and underside of tail.

Color: Rich, lustrous golden of various shades. Feathering may be lighter than rest of coat. With the exception of graying or whitening of face or body due to age, any white marking, other than a few white hairs on the chest, should be penalized according to its extent.

Gait: When trotting, gait is free, smooth, powerful and well co-ordinated, showing good reach.

Temperament: Friendly, reliable and trustworthy.

BODY
The body must be well balanced and short coupled.

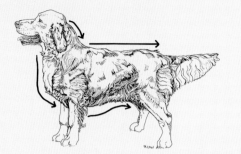

HEAD
The foreface should be deep and wide, nearly as long as skull, as shown on left. Incorrect head shown on right.

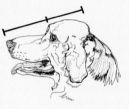

FORELEGS
The forelegs should be straight and the shoulders well laid back (left). Weak, narrow forequarters shown on right.

TAIL
The tail is carried level with back (left) never curling at the top. Incorrect tail shown on right.

GAIT
Stride is powerful and free with no sign of hackney action. Correct gait on left, hackney gait on right.

Finding a healthy, happy Golden puppy from an experienced breeder is the best path for the new owner. This pup is from Gold-Rush Kennels.

GOLDEN RETRIEVER

WHERE TO BEGIN

If you are convinced that the Golden Retriever is the ideal dog for you, it is time to learn about where to find a puppy and what to look for. Locating a litter of Golden Retrievers should not present a problem for the new owner. You should inquire about breeders in your area who enjoy a good reputation in the breed. You are looking for an established breeder with outstanding dog ethics and a strong commitment to the breed. New owners should have as many questions as they have doubts. An established breeder is indeed the one to answer your four million questions and make you comfortable with your choice of the Golden Retriever. An established breeder will sell you a puppy at a fair price if, and only if, the breeder determines that you are a suitable, worthy owner of his/her dogs. An established breeder can be relied upon for advice, no matter what time of day or night. A reputable breeder will accept a puppy back, without questions, should you decide that this not the right dog for you.

When choosing a breeder, reputation is much more important than convenience of location. Do not be overly impressed by breeders who run brag advertisements in the presses about their stupendous champions and working lines. The real quality breeders are quiet and unassuming. You hear about them at the dog trials and shows, by word of mouth. You may be well advised to avoid the novice who lives only a couple miles away. The local novice breeder,

YOUR SCHEDULE . . .

If you lead an erratic, unpredictable life, with daily or weekly changes in your work requirements, consider the problems of owning a puppy. The new puppy has to be fed regularly, socialized (loved, petted, handled, introduced to other people) and, most importantly, allowed to visit outdoors for house-training. As the dog gets older, it can be more tolerant of deviations in its feeding and outdoor relief.

trying so hard to get rid of that first litter of puppies, is more than accommodating and anxious to sell you one. That breeder will charge you as much as any established breeder. The novice breeder is not going to interrogate you and your family about your

breeders are devoted to the breed and its well-being. New owners should have little problem finding a reputable breeder who does not live on the other side of the country (or in a different country). The American Kennel Club is able to recommend breeders of quality Golden Retrievers, as can any local all-breed club or Golden Retriever club. Potential owners are encouraged to attend dog shows and obedience trials to see the Golden Retrievers in action; to get an idea what Golden Retrievers look like outside a photographer's lens. Provided you approach the handlers when they are not terribly busy with the dogs, most are more than willing to answer questions, recommend

When meeting with the breeder, be clear about what your intentions for your Golden Retriever will be. You cannot buy a pet-quality Golden and later decide that you want to show him. intentions with the puppy, the environment and training you can provide, etc. That breeder will be nowhere to be found when your poorly bred, badly adjusted four-pawed monster starts to growl and spit up at midnight or eat the family cat!

Socialization is a breeder concern of immense importance. Since the Golden Retriever's temperament can vary from line to line, socialization is the first and best way to encourage a proper, stable personality.

Choosing a breeder is an important first step in dog ownership. Fortunately, the majority of Golden Retriever

PUPPY SELECTION
Your selection of a good puppy can be determined by your needs. A show potential or a good pet? It is your choice. Every puppy, however, should be of good temperament. Although show-quality puppies are bred and raised with emphasis on physical conformation, responsible breeders strive for equally good temperament. Do not buy from a breeder who concentrates solely on physical beauty at the expense of personality.

Making a choice of which Golden puppy is best for you depends upon what you want in a dog. A show dog requires brains and beauty; a hunting dog requires stamina, trainability and musculature; a pet requires personality and soundness. All require good health and good breeding.

breeders and give advice.

Once you have contacted and met a breeder or two and made your choice about which breeder is best suited to your needs, it is time to visit the litter. Keep in mind that many top breeders have waiting lists. Sometimes new owners have to wait as long as two years for a puppy. If you are really committed to the breeder whom you have selected, then you will wait (and hope for an early arrival!). If not, you may have to go with your second- or third-choice breeder. Do not be too anxious, however. If the breeder does not have any waiting list, or any customers, there is probably a good reason. It is no different than visiting a restaurant with no clientele. The better cafés and restaurants always have a waiting list—and it is usually worth the wait. Besides, is not a puppy more important than a cup of java?

Since you are likely choosing a Golden Retriever as a pet dog and not a working dog, you simply should select a pup that is friendly and attractive. While the basic soundness of the breed is intact, the temperament may present trouble in certain strains. Beware of the shy or overly aggressive puppy; be

BREEDER RULES
Breeders rarely release puppies until they are eight to ten weeks of age. This is an acceptable age for most breeds of dog, excepting toy breeds which are not released until around 12 weeks, given their petite sizes. If a breeder has a puppy that is 12 weeks or older, it is likely well socialized and housetrained. Be sure that it is otherwise healthy before deciding to take it home.

especially conscious of the nervous Golden Retriever pup. Do not let sentiment or emotion trap you into buying the runt of the litter.

The gender of your puppy is largely a matter of personal taste, although there is a common belief among those who work with Golden Retrievers that

Bring the family along to assist in selecting the pup. The Golden you choose and each member of your family should share a mutual affinity for each other.

bitches are quicker to learn and generally more loving and faithful. Males learn more slowly but retain the lesson longer. The difference in size is noticeable but slight.

Breeders commonly allow visitors to see the litter by

around the fifth or sixth week, and puppies leave for their new homes between the eighth and tenth week. Breeders who permit their puppies to leave early are more interested in your money than their puppies' well-being. Puppies need to learn the rules of the trade from their dams, and most dams continue teaching the pups manners and dos and don'ts until around the eighth week. Breeders spend significant amounts of time with the Golden Retriever toddlers so that they are able to interact with the "other species," i.e., humans. Given the long history that dogs and humans have, bonding between the two species is natural but must be nurtured. A well-bred, well-socialized Golden Retriever pup wants nothing more than to be near you and please you.

COMMITMENT OF OWNERSHIP

After considering all of these factors, you have most likely already made some very important decisions about selecting your puppy. You have chosen a Golden Retriever, which means that you have decided which characteristics you want in a dog and what type of dog will best fit into your family and lifestyle. If you have selected a breeder, you have gone a step

STRESS-FREE

Some experts in canine health advise that stress during a dog's early years of development can compromise and weaken his immune system and may trigger the potential for a shortened life expectancy. They emphasize the need for happy and stress-free growing-up years.

When you buy a Golden Retriever puppy, you should get a copy of the registration and the pedigree. The breeder should be able to answer all of your questions about the kennel, health concerns and the breed in general.

the leaders, which ones are less outgoing, which ones are confident, which ones are shy, playful, friendly, aggressive, etc. Equally as important, you will learn to recognize what a healthy pup should look and act like. All of these things will help you in your search, and when you find the Golden Retriever that was meant for you, you will know it!

Researching your breed, further—you have done your research and found a responsible, conscientious person who breeds quality Golden Retrievers and who should be a reliable source of help as you and your puppy adjust to life together. If you have observed a litter in action, you have obtained a firsthand look at the dynamics of a puppy "pack" and, thus, you should learn about each pup's individual personality—perhaps you have even found one that particularly appeals to you.

However, even if you have not yet found the Golden Retriever puppy of your dreams, observing pups will help you learn to recognize certain behavior and to determine what a pup's behavior indicates about his temperament. You will be able to pick out which pups are

PEDIGREE VS. REGISTRATION CERTIFICATE

Too often new owners are confused between these two important documents. Your puppy's pedigree, essentially a family tree, is a written record of a dog's genealogy of three generations or more. The pedigree will show you the names as well as performance titles of all the dogs in your pup's background. Your breeder must provide you with a registration application, with his part properly filled out. You must complete the application and send it to the AKC with the proper fee. Every puppy must come from a litter that has been AKC-registered by the breeder, born in the USA and from a sire and dam that are also registered with the AKC.

The seller must provide you with complete records to identify the puppy. The AKC requires that the seller provide the buyer with the following: breed; sex, color and markings; date of birth; litter number (when available); names and registration numbers of the parents; breeder's name; and date sold or delivered.

Golden Retrievers typically have large litters, sometimes as many as a dozen puppies. Potential buyers have many adorable contestants to review.

selecting a responsible breeder and observing as many pups as possible are all important steps on the way to dog ownership. It may seem like a lot of effort... and you have not

PUPPY APPEARANCE

Your puppy should have a well-fed appearance but not a distended abdomen, which may indicate worms or incorrect feeding, or both. The body should be firm, with a solid feel. The skin of the abdomen should be pale pink and clean, without signs of scratching or rash. Check the legs to see if dewclaws were removed, as this is done at only a few day old.

even brought the pup home yet! Remember, though, you cannot be too careful when it comes to deciding on the type of dog you want and finding out about your prospective pup's background. Buying a puppy is not—or should not be—just another whimsical purchase. This is one instance in which you actually do get to choose your own family! You may be thinking that buying a puppy should be fun— it should not be so serious and so much work. Keep in mind that your puppy is not a cuddly stuffed toy or decorative lawn ornament, but a creature that will become a real member of your family. You will come to realize that, while buying a puppy is a pleasurable and exciting

endeavor, it is not something to be taken lightly. Relax...the fun will start when the pup comes home!

Always keep in mind that a puppy is nothing more than a baby in a furry disguise...a baby who is virtually helpless in a human world and who trusts his owner for fulfilment of his basic needs for survival. In addition to food, water and shelter, your pup needs care, protection, guidance and love. If you are not prepared to commit to this, then you are not prepared to own a dog.

You should think long-term when you consider buying a dog of any breed. Food, veterinary care, training, possibly doggie day care, are short-term as well as lifetime expenses and will seriously impact your budget. You must allow for your pup's initial veterinary care as well as the future and ongoing costs of routine shots and check-ups, spaying/neutering, possible emergency care and medications for the inevitable canine illnessses your dog may experience. And as with a sick child, canine emergencies need attention now, not later when you collect a bonus or commission.

Wait a minute, you say. How hard could this be? All of my neighbors own dogs and they seem to be doing just fine. Why should I have to worry about all

Don't forget that you are not buying a stuffed doll. With ownership comes responsibility. Your Golden puppy will depend upon you for food, shelter, training and companionship.

of this? Well, you should not worry about it; in fact, you will probably find that once your Golden Retriever pup gets used to his new home, he will fall into his place in the family quite naturally. But it never hurts to emphasize the commitment of dog ownership. With some time and patience, it is really not too difficult to raise a curious and exuberant Golden Retriever pup to be a well-adjusted and well-

WHAT'S ILP?

If you have acquired a puppy and have no interest in showing or breeding, you can apply for an ILP or an Indefinite Listing Privilege, which affords your dog the opportunity to participate in obedience, agility, tracking and many other performance events. An ILP does not replace the dog's registration certification, and all ILPs must belong to an AKC-recognized breed and be spayed or neutered.

Your vet should examine your new Golden acquisition and evaluate its overall condition and health. He will also prescribe a program of inoculations against major canine diseases.

mannered adult dog—a dog that could be your most loyal friend.

PREPARING PUPPY'S PLACE IN YOUR HOME

Researching your breed and finding a breeder are only two aspects of the "homework" you will have to do before bringing your Golden Retriever puppy home. You will also have to prepare your home and family for the new addition. Much like you would prepare a nursery for a newborn baby, you will need to designate a place in your home that will be the puppy's own. How you prepare your home will depend on how much freedom the dog will be allowed. Will he be confined to one room or a specific area in the house, or will he be allowed to roam as he pleases? Whatever you decide, you must ensure that he has a place that he can "call his own."

When you bring your new puppy into your home, you are bringing him into what will

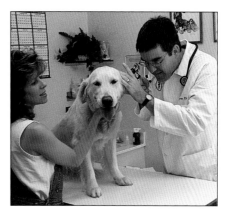

become his home as well. Obviously, you did not buy a puppy so that he could take over your house, but in order for a puppy to grow into a stable, well-adjusted dog, he has to feel comfortable in his surroundings. Remember, he is leaving the warmth and security of his mother and littermates, as well as the familiarity of the only place he has ever known, so it is important to make his transition as easy as possible. By preparing a place in your home for the puppy, you are making him feel as welcome as possible in a strange new place. It should not take him long to get used to it, but the sudden shock of being transplanted is somewhat traumatic for a young pup. Imagine how a small child would feel in the same situation—that is how your puppy must be feeling. It is up to you to reassure him and to let him know, "Little buddy, you are going to like it here!"

MALE OR FEMALE?

An important consideration to be discussed is the sex of your puppy. For a family companion, a bitch may be the better choice, considering the female's inbred concern for all young creatures and her accompanying tolerance and patience. It is always advised to spay a pet bitch, which may guarantee her a longer life.

WHAT YOU SHOULD BUY

CRATE

To someone unfamiliar with the use of crates in dog training, it may seem like punishment to shut a dog in a crate, but this is not the case at all. Crates are not cruel—crates have many humane and highly effective uses in dog care and training. For example, crate training is a very popular and very successful housebreaking method. A crate can keep your dog safe during travel; and, perhaps most importantly, a crate provides your dog with a place of his own in your home. It serves as a "doggie bedroom" of sorts—your Golden Retriever can curl up in his crate when he wants to sleep or when he just needs a break. Many dogs sleep in their crates

overnight. When lined with soft blankets and a favorite toy, a crate becomes a cozy pseudo-den for your dog. Like his ancestors, he too will seek out the comfort and retreat of a den—you just happen to be providing him with something a little more luxurious than leaves and twigs lining a dirty ditch.

As far as purchasing a crate, the type that you buy is up to you. It will most likely be one of the two most popular types: wire

> You have just brought your Golden Retriever puppy home. Are you prepared for the first night? Have you obtained the necessities?

PREPARING FOR PUP

Unfortunately, when a puppy is bought by someone who does not take into consideration the time and attention that dog ownership requires, it is the puppy who suffers when he is either abandoned or placed in a shelter by a frustrated owner. So all of the "homework" you do in preparation for your pup's arrival will benefit you both. The more informed you are, the more you will know what to expect and the better equipped you will be to handle the ups and downs of raising a puppy. Hopefully, everyone in the household is willing to do his part in raising and caring for the pup. The anticipation of owning a dog often brings a lot of promises from excited family members: "I will walk him every day," "I will feed him," "I will housebreak him," etc., but these things take time and effort, and promises can easily be forgotten once the novelty of the new pet has worn off.

forever—in fact, sometimes it seems as if they grow right before your eyes. A Yorkie-sized crate may be fine for a very young Golden Retriever pup, but it will not do him much good for long! Unless you have the money and the inclination to buy a new crate every time your pup has a growth spurt, it is better to get one that will accommodate your dog both as a pup and at full size. A large-size crate will be necessary for a full-grown Golden Retriever, who stands approximately 24 inches high.

BEDDING
A blanket or two in the dog's crate will help the dog feel more at home. First, the blankets will take the place of the leaves, twigs, etc., that the pup would use in the wild to make a den; the pup can make his own "burrow" in the crate. Although your pup is far removed from

No creature is more impressionable than a young Golden Retriever. Embark on your pup's training with kindness and consistency and you will be rewarded with an obedient companion.

or fiberglass. There are advantages and disadvantages to each type. For example, a wire crate is more open, allowing the air to flow through and affording the dog a view of what is going on around him. A fiberglass crate, however, is sturdier and can double as a travel crate since it provides more protection for the dog. The size of the crate is another thing to consider. Puppies do not stay puppies

A MOUTHFUL
Never house your Golden puppy in a kennel run with gravel or similar flooring. Golden puppies are notorious chewers and will happily dine on small, loose stones. Veterinarians' stories abound about puppies who are presented for emergency surgery because they have ingested objects thought to be impossible to swallow.

his den-making ancestors, the denning instinct is still a part of his genetic makeup. Second, until you bring your pup home, he has been sleeping amid the warmth of his mother and litter-mates, and while a blanket is not the same as a warm, breathing body, it still provides heat and something with which to snuggle. You will want to wash your pup's blankets frequently in case he has an accident in his crate, and replace or remove any blanket that becomes ragged and starts to fall apart.

Toys

Toys are a must for dogs of all ages, especially for curious playful pups. Puppies are the "children" of the dog world, and what child does not love toys? Chew toys provide enjoyment to both dog and owner—your dog will enjoy playing with his favorite toys, while you will enjoy the fact that they distract him from your expensive shoes and leather sofa. Puppies love to chew; in fact, chewing is a physical need for pups as they are teething, and everything looks appetizing! The full range of your possessions—from old dishrag to Oriental rug—are fair game in the eyes of a teething pup. Puppies are not all that discerning when it comes to finding something to literally "sink their teeth into"—

Many top breeders recommend the use of a crate in training. Your local pet shop should have a full range of dog crates from which you can select the size, style and color of your preference.

PHOTO COURTESY OF MIKKI PET PRODUCTS

everything tastes great!

Golden Retriever puppies are fairly aggressive chewers and only the hardest, strongest toys should be offered to them. Breeders advise owners to resist stuffed toys, because they can become de-stuffed in no time. The overly excited pup may ingest the stuffing, which is neither digestible nor nutritious.

Similarly, squeaky toys are quite popular, but must be avoided for the Golden Retriever. Perhaps a squeaky toy can be

Your local pet shop will have a wide assortment of dog toys. Do not offer your dog toys designed for children. Human toys can be dangerous because they are usually too flimsy and may contain dangerous dyes.

CRATE TRAINING

During crate training, you should partition off the section of the crate in which the pup stays. If he is given too big an area, this will hinder your training efforts. Crate training is based on the fact that a dog does not like to soil his sleeping quarters, so it is ineffective to keep a pup in a crate that is so big that he can eliminate in one end and get far enough away from it to sleep. Also, you want to make the crate den-like for the pup. Blankets and a favorite toy will make the crate cozy for the small pup; as he grows, you may want to evict some of his "roommates" to make more room.

used as an aid in training, but not for free play. If a pup "disembowels" one of these, the small plastic squeaker inside can be dangerous if swallowed. Monitor the condition of all your pup's toys carefully and get rid of any that have been chewed to the point of becoming potentially dangerous.

Be careful of natural bones, which have a tendency to splinter into sharp, dangerous pieces. Also be careful of rawhide, which can turn into pieces that are easy to swallow or into a mushy mess on your carpet.

GETTING TO KNOW YOU

It will take at least two weeks for your puppy to become accustomed to his new surroundings. Give him lots of love, attention, handling, frequent opportunities to relieve himself, a diet he likes to eat and a place he can call his own.

LEAD

A nylon lead is probably the best option as it is the most resistant to puppy teeth should your pup take a liking to chewing on his lead. Of course, this is a habit that should be nipped in the bud, but if your pup likes to chew on his lead he has a very

The retriever breeds are the most oral of all dogs. While a young pup's nip is harmless, an owner must discourage such behavior at once.

Golden Retrievers have very strong, sharp teeth that are capable of destroying most ordinary toys. Offer safe, durable chew toys to your dog.

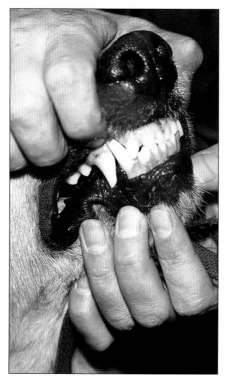

are special leads for training purposes, and specially made leather harnesses for working Golden Retrievers, but these are not necessary for routine walks.

COLLAR
Your pup should get used to wearing a collar all the time since you will want to attach his ID tags to it. Plus, you have to attach the lead to something! A lightweight nylon collar is a good choice; make sure that it fits snugly enough so that the pup cannot wriggle out of it, but is loose enough so that it will not be uncomfortably tight around the pup's neck. You should be able to fit a finger between the pup and the collar. It may take some time for your pup to get used to wearing the collar, but soon he will not even notice that

slim chance of being able to chew through the strong nylon. Nylon leads are also lightweight, which is good for a young Golden Retriever who is just getting used to the idea of walking on a lead. For everyday walking and safety purposes, the nylon lead is a good choice. As your pup grows up and gets used to walking on the lead, you may want to purchase a flexible lead. These leads allow you to extend the length to give the dog a broader area to explore or to shorten the length to keep the dog close to you. Of course there

PUPPY PROBLEMS
The majority of problems that are commonly seen in young pups will disappear as your dog gets older. However, how you deal with problems when he is young will determine how he reacts to discipline as an adult dog. It is important to establish who is boss (hopefully it will be you!) right away when you are first bonding wiith your dog. This bond will set the tone for the rest of your life together.

TOYS, TOYS, TOYS

With a big variety of dog toys available, and so many that look like they would be a lot of fun for a dog, be careful in your selection. It is amazing what a set of puppy teeth can do to an innocent-looking toy, so, obviously, safety is a major consideration. Be sure to choose the most durable products that you can find. Hard nylon bones and toys are a safe bet, and many of them are offered in different scents and flavors that will be sure to capture your dog's attention. It is always fun to play a game of catch with your dog, and there are balls and flying discs that are specially made to withstand dog teeth.

it is there. Choke collars are made for training, but should only be used by an experienced handler.

FOOD AND WATER BOWLS

Your pup will need two bowls, one for food and one for water. You may want two sets of bowls, one for inside and one for outside, depending on where the dog will be fed and where he will be spending time. Stainless steel or sturdy plastic bowls are popular choices. Plastic bowls are more chewable. Dogs tend not to chew on the steel variety, which can be sterilized. It is important to buy sturdy bowls since anything is in danger of being chewed by puppy teeth

and you do not want your dog to be constantly chewing apart his bowl (for his safety and for your wallet!).

CLEANING SUPPLIES

Until a pup is housetrained, you will be doing a lot of cleaning. "Accidents" will occur, which is okay in the beginning because the puppy does not know any better. All you can do is be prepared to clean up any accidents. Old rags, towels, newspapers and a safe disinfectant are good to have on hand.

BEYOND THE BASICS

The items previously discussed are the bare necessities. You will find out what else you need as you go along—grooming supplies, flea/tick protection, baby gates to partition a room, etc. These things will vary depending on your situation but it is important that you have

Puppies learn from watching. If you are bringing a second dog into the household, the puppy will follow the older dog's example—a great aid in lead training and lots more.

everything you need to feed and make your Golden Retriever comfortable in his first few days at home.

PUPPY-PROOFING YOUR HOME

Aside from making sure that your Golden Retriever will be comfortable in your home, you also have to make sure that your home is safe for your Golden Retriever. This means taking precautions that your pup will not get into anything he should not get into and that there is nothing within his reach that may harm him should he sniff it, chew it, inspect it, etc. This probably seems obvious since, while you are primarily concerned with your pup's safety, at the same time you do

You should always clean up after your dog. Pet shops sell special tools that enable you to perform this essential task as simply as possible.

> **FEEDING TIPS**
> You will probably start feeding your pup the same food that he has been getting from the breeder; the breeder should give you a few days' supply to start you off. Although you should not give your pup too many treats, you will want to have puppy treats on hand for coaxing, training, rewards, etc. Be careful, though, as a small pup's calorie requirements are relatively low and a few treats can add up to almost a full day's worth of calories without the required nutrition.

not want your belongings to be ruined. Breakables should be placed out of reach if your dog is to have full run of the house. If he is to be limited to certain places within the house, keep any potentially dangerous items in the "off-limits" areas. An electrical cord can pose a danger should the puppy decide to taste it—and who is going to convince a pup that it would not make a great chew toy? Cords should be fastened tightly against the wall. If your dog is going to spend time in a crate, make sure that there is nothing near his crate that he can reach if he sticks his curious little nose or paws through the openings. Just as you would with a child, keep all household cleaners and chemicals where the pup cannot get to them.

It is also important to make sure that the outside of your home is safe. Of course your puppy should never be unsupervised, but a pup let loose in the yard will want to run and explore, and he should be granted that freedom. Do not let a fence give you a false sense of security; you would be surprised how crafty (and persistent) a dog can be in figuring out how to dig under and squeeze his way through small holes, or to jump or climb over a fence. The remedy is to make the fence high enough

Stainless steel or sturdy plastic food and water bowls are good choices for your Golden. Also necessary are stands on which to elevate the bowls as a bloat preventative.

PHOTO COURTESY OF MIKKI PET PRODUCTS

PUPPY-PROOFING

Thoroughly puppy-proof your house before bringing your puppy home. Never use roach or rodent poisons in any area accessible to the puppy. Avoid the use of toilet bowl cleaners. Most dogs are born with toilet bowl sonar and will take a drink if the lid is left open. Also keep the trash secured and out of reach.

so that it really is impossible for your dog to get over it (about 3 yards should suffice), and well embedded into the ground. Be sure to repair or secure any gaps

in the fence. Check the fence periodically to ensure that it is in good shape and make repairs as needed; a very determined pup may return to the same spot to "work on it" until he is able to get through.

FIRST TRIP TO THE VET
You have picked out your puppy, and your home and family are ready. Now all you have to do is collect your Golden Retriever from the breeder and the fun begins, right? Well…not so fast. Something else you need to prepare is your pup's first trip to the veterinarian. Perhaps the breeder can recommend someone in the area who specializes in Golden Retrievers, or maybe you know some other Golden

> **INVISIBLE FENCES**
> The electrical fencing system, which forms an invisible fence, works on a battery-operated collar that shocks the dog if it gets too close to the buried (or elevated) wire. There are some people who think very highly of this system of controlling a dog's wandering. Keep in mind that the collar has batteries. For safety's sake, replace the batteries every month with the best quality batteries available.

Retriever owners who can suggest a good vet. Either way, you should have an appointment arranged for your pup before you pick him up and plan on taking him for an examination before bringing him home.

The pup's first visit will consist of an overall examination to make sure that the pup does not have any problems that are not apparent to you. The veterinarian will also set up a schedule for the pup's vaccinations; the breeder will inform you of which ones the pup has already received and the vet can continue from there.

INTRODUCTION TO THE FAMILY
Everyone in the house will be excited about the puppy's coming home and will want to pet him and play with him, but it is best to make the introduc-

Keep your eye on your dog when your flowers bloom. The scent brings both retrievers (they have very sensitive noses) and biting insects together. Blooming flowers should be off-limits to your Golden. Goldens are frequently allergic to flower pollen.

tions low-key so as not to overwhelm the puppy. He is apprehensive already. It is the first time he has been separated from his mother and the breeder, and the ride to your home is likely the first time he has been in a car. The last thing you want to do is smother him, as this will only frighten him further. This is not to say that human contact is not extremely necessary at this stage, because this is the time when a connection between the pup and his human family is formed. Gentle petting and soothing words should help console him, as well as just putting him down and letting him explore on his own (under your watchful eye, of course).

The pup may approach the family members or may busy himself with exploring for a while. Gradually, each person should spend some time with the pup, one at a time, crouching down to get as close to the pup's level as possible, letting him sniff their hands and petting him gently. He definitely needs human attention and he needs to be touched—this is how to form an immediate bond. Just remember that the pup is experiencing a lot of things for the first time, at the same time. There are new people, new noises, new smells and new things to investigate: so be gentle, be

If you own a Golden Retriever, you must have a trusted vet to maintain your dog in good health, to arrange a vaccination schedule and to recommend the most up-to-date medications as needed.

affectionate and be as comforting as you can be.

YOUR PUP'S FIRST NIGHT HOME
You have traveled home with your new charge safely in his crate. He has been to the vet for a thorough check-up; he has been weighed, his papers examined; perhaps he has even been vaccinated and wormed as

PUPPY EXPENSES
Grooming tools, collars, leashes, dog beds and, of course, toys will be an expense to you when you first obtain your pup, and the cost will trickle on throughout your dog's lifetime. If your puppy damages or destroys your possessions (as most puppies surely will!) or something belonging to a neighbor, you can calculate additional expense. There is also parasite control, which every dog owner faces more than once. You must be able to handle the financial responsibility of owning a dog.

well. He has met the family, and he's licked the whole family, including the excited children and the less-than-happy cat. He has explored his area, his new bed, the yard and anywhere else he has been permitted. He has eaten his first meal at home and relieved himself in the proper place. He has heard lots of new sounds, smelled new friends and

TRAINING TIP
Training your puppy takes much patience and can be frustrating at times, but you should see results from your efforts. If you have a puppy that seems untrainable, take him to a trainer or behaviorist. The dog may have a personality problem that requires the help of a professional, or perhaps you need help in learning how to train your dog.

Even a frightened Golden Retriever will welcome attention from his new family members. Most Golden pups adjust quite easily to their new environment.

seen more of the outside world than ever before.

That was just the first day! He has tuckered out and is ready for bed...or so you think!

It is puppy's first night and you are ready to say "Good night"—keep in mind that this is puppy's first night ever to be sleeping alone. His dam and littermates are no longer at paw's length and he is a bit scared, cold and lonely. Be reassuring to your new family member. This is not the time to spoil him and give in to his inevitable whining.

Puppies whine. They whine to let the others know where they are and hopefully to get company out of it. Place your pup in his new crate in his room and close the door. Mercifully, he may fall asleep without a peep. When the inevitable occurs, ignore the whining: he is fine. Be strong

Puppy's first night can be somewhat stressful for the pup and his new family. Remember that you are setting the tone of nighttime at your house. Unless you want to play with

Breeders arrange for their puppies to meet new people while still with their dam. These pups are always the best socialized.

and keep his interest in mind. Do not allow your heart to become guilty and visit the pup. He will fall asleep.

Some breeders suggest moving the crate into your bedroom at night for the first several weeks. Sleeping in your room will not spoil the puppy. It will make him feel secure and continue the bonding process throughout the night. Beyond that, if the puppy needs to relieve himself during the night, you will be able to whisk him out immediately. Do not ever give in and remove him from his crate or allow him into bed with you.

Many breeders recommend placing a piece of bedding from his former homestead in his new bed so that he recognizes the scent of his littermates. Others still advise placing a hot water bottle in his bed for warmth. This latter may be a good idea provided the pup does not attempt to suckle—he will get good and wet and may not fall asleep so fast.

CHEWING TIPS

Chewing goes hand in hand with nipping in the sense that a teething puppy is always looking for a way to soothe his aching gums. In this case, instead of chewing on you, he may have taken a liking to your favorite shoe or something else which he should not be chewing. Again, realize that this is a normal canine behavior that does not need to be discouraged, only redirected. Your pup just needs to be taught what is acceptable to chew on and what is off-limits. Consistently tell him "No" when you catch him chewing on something forbidden and give him a chew toy. Conversely, praise him when you catch him chewing on something appropriate. In this way, you are discouraging the inappropriate behavior and reinforcing the desired behavior. The puppy's chewing should stop after his adult teeth have come in, but an adult dog continues to chew for various reasons—perhaps because he is bored, needs to relieve tension or just likes to chew. That is why it is important to redirect his chewing when he is still young.

your pup every evening at 10 p.m., midnight and 2 a.m., do not initiate the habit. Your family will thank you, and so will your pup!

PREVENTING PUPPY PROBLEMS

SOCIALIZATION

Now that you have done all of the preparatory work and have helped your pup get accustomed to his new home and family, it is about time for you to have some fun! Socializing your Golden Retriever pup gives you the opportunity to show off your new friend, and your pup gets to reap the benefits of being an adorable furry creature that people will coo over, want to pet and, in general, think is absolutely precious!

Besides getting to know his new family, your puppy should be exposed to other people, animals and situations. This will help him become well adjusted as he grows up and less prone to being timid or fearful of the new things he will encounter. Your pup's socialization began at the breeder's kennel but now it is your responsibility to continue it. The socialization he receives up until the age of 16 to 20 weeks is the most critical, as this is the time when he forms his impressions of the outside world. Be especially careful during the eight-to-ten-week-old period, also known as the fear period. The interaction he receives during this time should be gentle and reassuring. Lack of

THE RIDE HOME

Taking your dog from the breeder to your home in a car can be a very uncomfortable experience for both of you. The puppy will have been taken from his warm, friendly, safe environment and brought into a strange new environment. An environment that moves! Be prepared for loose bowels, urination, crying, whining and even fear biting. With proper love and encouragement when you arrive home, the stress of the trip should quickly disappear.

socialization can manifest itself in fear and aggression as the dog grows up. He needs lots of human contact, affection, handling and exposure to other animals.

Once your pup has received his necessary vaccinations, feel free to take him out and about (on his lead, of course). Walk him around the neighborhood, take him on your daily errands, let people pet him, let him meet other dogs and pets, etc. Puppies do not have to try to make friends; there will be no shortage of people who will want to introduce themselves. Just make sure that you carefully supervise each meeting. If the neighborhood children want to say hello, for example, that is great—children and pups most often make great companions. Sometimes an excited child can unintentionally handle a pup too roughly, or an overzealous

MEET THE WORLD
Thorough socialization includes not only meeting new people but also being introduced to new experiences such as riding in the car, having his coat brushed, hearing the television, walking in a crowd—the list is endless. The more your pup experiences, and the more positive the experiences are, the less shocking and scary it will be for your pup to encounter new things.

pup can playfully nip a little too hard. You want to make socialization experiences positive ones. What a pup learns during this very formative stage will impact his attitude toward future encounters. You want your dog to be comfortable around everyone. A pup that has a bad experience with a child may grow up to be a dog that is shy around or aggressive toward children.

CONSISTENCY IN TRAINING

Dogs, being pack animals, naturally need a leader, or else they try to establish dominance in their packs. When you bring a dog into your family, the choice of who becomes the leader and who becomes the "pack" is entirely up to you! Your pup's intuitive quest for dominance, coupled with the fact that it is nearly impossible to look at an

Puppies should be accustomed to relieving themselves outdoors in designated areas. This is called housebreaking.

Your Golden's first "pack" is his litter, led by his dam. Your family becomes his new pack, and you, his new leader.

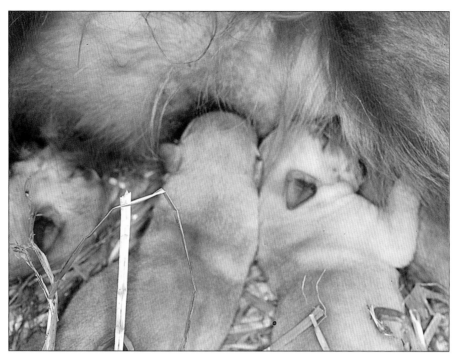

adorable Golden Retriever pup, with his "puppy-dog" eyes and his too-big-for-his-head-still-floppy ears, and not cave in, give the pup almost an unfair advantage in getting the upper hand! A pup will definitely test the waters to see what he can and cannot do. Do not give in to those pleading eyes—stand your ground when it comes to disciplining the pup and make sure that all family members do the same. It will only confuse the pup when Mother tells him to get off the couch when he is used to sitting up there with Father to watch the nightly news.

Avoid discrepancies by having all members of the household decide on the rules before the pup even comes home...and be consistent in enforcing them! Early training shapes the dog's personality, so you cannot be unclear in what you expect.

You may want to attend a puppy class and early obedience training with your puppy. A class environment is good social stimulation for the puppy and for you. It will also motivate you to train your puppy and practice when you are not in class so you do not appear foolish in front of your trainer and fellow puppy

owners. Investigate the cost of puppy lessons so you do not omit this important aspect of Golden ownership.

COMMON PUPPY PROBLEMS

The best way to prevent puppy problems is to be proactive in stopping an undesirable behavior as soon as it starts. The old saying "You can't teach an old dog new tricks" does not necessarily hold true, but it is true that it is much easier to discourage bad behavior in a young developing pup than to wait until the pup's bad behavior becomes the adult dog's bad habit. There are some problems that are especially prevalent in puppies as they develop.

NIPPING

As puppies start to teethe, they feel the need to sink their teeth into anything available... unfortunately that includes your fingers, arms, hair, and toes. You may find this behavior cute for the first five seconds...until you feel just how sharp those puppy teeth are. This is something you want to discourage immediately and consistently with a firm "No!" (or whatever number of firm "No's" it takes for him to understand that you mean business). Then replace your finger with an appropriate chew toy. While this behavior is merely annoying when the dog is young, it can become dangerous as your Golden Retriever's adult teeth grow in and his jaws develop, and he

Puppies enjoy all kinds of toys, especially stuffed animals that squeak. Do not allow children to provoke the puppy as this can lead to nipping.

continues to think it is okay to gnaw on human appendages. This is a very oral breed with a natural tendency to chew and nip. He does not mean any harm with a friendly nip, but he also does not know his own strength.

CRYING/WHINING

Your pup will often cry, whine, whimper, howl or make some type of commotion when he is left alone. This is basically his way of calling out for attention to make sure that you know he is there and that you have not forgotten about him. He feels insecure when he is left alone, when you are out of the house and he is in his crate or when you are in another part of the house and he cannot see you. The noise he is making is an expression of the anxiety he feels at being alone, so he needs to be taught that being alone is okay. You are not actually training the dog to stop making noise, you are training him to feel comfortable when he is alone and thus removing the need for him to make the noise. This is where the crate filled with cozy blankets and a toy comes in handy. You want to know that he is safe when you are not there to supervise, and you know that he will be safe in his crate rather than roaming freely

about the house. In order for the pup to stay in his crate without making a fuss, he needs to be comfortable in his crate. On that note, it is extremely important that the crate is never used as a form of punishment, or the pup will have a negative association with the crate.

Accustom the pup to the crate in short, gradually increasing time intervals in which you put him in the crate, maybe with a treat, and stay in the room with him. If he cries or makes a fuss, do not go to him, but stay in his sight. Gradually he will realize that staying in his crate is all right without your help, and it will not be so traumatic for him when you are not around. You may want to leave the radio on softly when you leave the house; the sound of human voices may be comforting to him.

CHEMICAL ALERT
Scour your garage for potential puppy dangers. Remove weed killers, pesticides and antifreeze materials. Antifreeze is highly toxic and even a few drops can kill an adult dog. The sweet taste attracts the animal, who will quickly consume it from the floor or curbside.

POISONOUS PLANTS

Below is a partial list of plants that are considered poisonous. These plants can cause skin irritation, illness and even death. You should be aware of the types of plants that grow in your yard and that you keep in your home. Special care should be taken to rid your yard of dangerous plants and to keep all plants in the household out of your Golden Retriever's reach.

American Blue Flag	Japanese Yew
Bachelor's Button	Jerusalem Cherry
Barberry	Jimson Weed
Bog Iris	Lenten Rose
Boxwood	Lily of the Valley
Buttercup	Marigold
Cherry Pits	Milkwort
Chinese Arbor	Mistletoe (berries)
Chokecherry	Monkshood
Christmas Rose	Mullein
Climbing Lily	Narcissus
Crown of Thorns	Peony
Elderberry (berries)	Persian Ivy
Elephant Ear	Rhododendron
English Ivy	Rhubarb
False Acacia	Shallon
Fern	Siberian Iris
Foxglove	Solomon's Seal
Hellebore	Star of Bethlehem
Herb of Grace	Water Lily
Holly	Wisteria
Horse Chestnut	Wood Spurge
Iris (bulb)	Yew

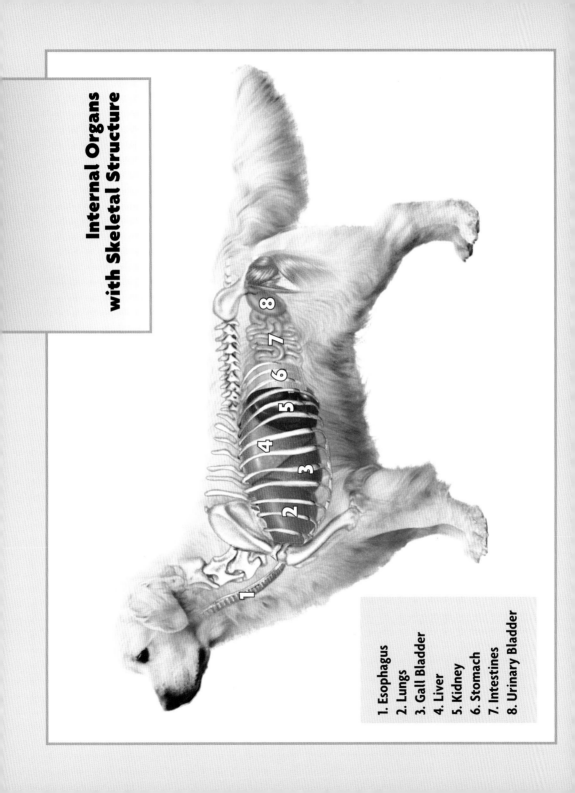

Internal Organs with Skeletal Structure

1. Esophagus
2. Lungs
3. Gall Bladder
4. Liver
5. Kidney
6. Stomach
7. Intestines
8. Urinary Bladder

GOLDEN RETRIEVER

The responsibility of owning a Golden Retriever is a long-term commitment that will affect your life every day as you care for your growing puppy and mature adult. The author has owned as many as eight Goldens at a time, yet even the keeping of one dog is an enormous job. Owners must be properly informed about the feeding of the Golden Retriever, the grooming and exercise requirements and much more. Let's begin by looking at the various aspects of feeding the Golden Retriever.

DIETARY AND FEEDING CONSIDERATIONS

You have probably heard it a thousand times, "You are what you eat." Believe it or not, it's very true. Dogs are what you feed them because they have little choice in the matter. Even those people who truly want to feed their dogs the best often cannot do so because they do not know which foods are best for their dogs.

Dog foods are produced in three basic types: dry, semi-moist and canned. Dry foods are the choice of the cost-conscious because they are much less expensive than semi-moist and canned. Dry foods contain the least fat and the most preservatives. Most canned foods are 60–70-percent water, while semi-moist foods are so full of sugar that they are the least preferred by owners, though dogs welcome them (as a child does sweets). You must always feed your Golden a quality food, and such a product will cost more than generic and over-the-counter brands sold at a local grocery store.

Pet shops sell the premium brands of dog food, which are

Golden Retrievers simply must be fed a proper, balanced diet in order to stay healthy and fit.

designed for pure-bred performance animals, whether show dogs, field dogs or the like. These premium brands are the ones recommended by vets and breeders for pure-bred pet dogs as well. Unlike the store brands, which are cheaper in price and quality, the premium foods contain less filler and more meat products. The price you pay for premium dog food will be reflected in your dog's coat, overall health and temperament. Quality foods contain balanced nutrition for your dog, so that supplementation is not necessary, though you should discuss this with your breeder. Some breeders contend that a complete diet could never "come in a bag," just as you could not expect a human child to grow up properly only eating a dry cereal. Thus, some of these breeders add vegetables, eggs and fresh meat to their dogs' diets on occasion to give them some natural nourishment. Most agree that such supplementation does not harm the dog, though it could make the dog more fussy. Further, many object to the preservatives in the dry food, which give the "complete diet" a shelf life of a year or more.

Three stages of development must be considered when selecting

FOOD PREFERENCE

Selecting the best dry dog food is difficult. There is no majority consensus among veterinary scientists as to the value of nutrient analyses (protein, fat, fiber, moisture, ash, cholesterol, minerals, etc.). All agree that feeding trials are what matter, but you also have to consider the individual dog. Its weight, age, activity and what pleases its taste all must be considered. It is probably best to take the advice of your veterinarian. Every dog's dietary requirements vary, even during the lifetime of that particular dog.

If your dog is fed a good dry food, it does not require supplements of meat or vegetables. Dogs do appreciate a little variety in their diets so you may choose to stay with the same brand, but vary the flavor. Alternatively you may wish to add a little flavored stock to give a difference to the taste.

TEST FOR PROPER DIET
A good test for proper diet is the color, odor and firmness of your dog's stool. A healthy dog usually produces three semi-hard stools per day. The stools should have no unpleasant odor. They should be the same color from excretion to excretion.

a diet for your dog: the puppy stage, the adult stage and the senior or geriatric stage.

PUPPY STAGE
Puppies have a natural instinct to suck milk from their mother's teats. They exhibit this behavior from the first moments of their lives. If they don't suckle within a short while, the breeder attempts to put them onto their mother's nipples. A newborn's failure to suckle often requires that the breeder handfeed the pup under the guidance of a veterinarian. This involves a baby bottle and a special formula. Their mother's milk is much better than any formula because it contains colostrum, a sort of antibiotic milk that protects the puppy during the first eight to ten weeks of their lives.

Puppies should be allowed to nurse for six weeks and they should be slowly weaned away from their mother by introducing small portions of canned food after they are about one month old. Then dry food is gradually added to the puppies' portions over the next few weeks. By the time they are eight weeks old, they should be completely weaned and fed solely a puppy kibble. During this weaning period, their diet is most important as the

Golden Retriever puppies should be allowed to nurse for at least six weeks. The last two weeks of this period should begin the slow introduction of canned food.

Once a puppy is in your home, it may not eat as vigorously as it did while at the breeder's home. Competition for food at the feed tray entices the puppies' appetites.

Hand-feeding pups when the need arises requires an excellent-quality formula and diligent attention from the breeder.

puppy grows fastest during its first year of life.

Golden Retriever pups should be fed three meals per day when they are six to eight weeks of age. At eight weeks, the pup can be fed twice per day. Fussy eaters may require an additional smaller meal to maintain a good weight. Growth foods can be recommended by your veterinarian, and the puppy should be kept on this diet for up to 12 months. Puppy diets should be balanced for your dog's needs, and supplements of vitamins, minerals and protein should not be necessary.

ADULT DIETS

A dog is considered an adult when it has stopped growing in height and/or length. Do not consider the dog's weight when the decision is made to switch from a puppy diet to an adult maintenance diet. Again you should rely upon your veteri-

narian to recommend an acceptable maintenance diet. Major dog food manufacturers specialize in this type of food, and it is necessary for you to select the one best suited to your dog's needs. Active dogs may have different requirements than sedate dogs. A Golden Retriever is fully mature around 12 months of age, though it often takes another 12 to 18 months for dog to reach its peak as a performance animal.

Discuss the diet of your active Golden Retriever with your veterinarian or breeder. Some dogs require more food to maintain their weight than others. Also discuss supplementing your Golden's diet with fresh foods with your breeder. Every dog welcomes fresh meat in his diet, and most dogs show an interest in vegetables as well. Experiment to see what your Golden likes. Provided you don't overdo these supplements, you will be adding to your dog's nutrition. You

also may wish to discuss vitamin and mineral supplements with your breeder, which may or may not be of value to your dog. A good barometer for the quality of your dog's food comes from the other end of the dog. If your dog's stool seem loose or excessive, the food he's eating is likely more filler than meat. Since Goldens are prone to bloat, it's advised that you test your dog's food before choosing a brand. Most manufacturers are happy to provide you with a sample of their brand. Place a few pieces of the dry food into a glass of water. If the food swells to five or six times its original size, it is not recommended for the Golden. This is how the food will react in your dog's stomach, and that is not acceptable in a deep-chest breed that is prone to bloat.

Clean water should be available to all dogs. Golden Retriever puppies would often rather swim in water than drink it!

GRAIN-BASED DIETS

Some less expensive dog foods are based on grains and other plant proteins. While these products may appear to be attractively priced, many breeders prefer a diet based on animal proteins and believe that they are more conducive to your dog's health. Many grain-based diets rely on soy protein, which may cause flatulence (passing gas).

There are many cases, however, when your dog might require a special diet. These special requirements should only be recommended by your veterinarian.

As your Golden Retriever matures, his dietary needs change. Active working dogs will require a different nutritional base than will ordinary house dogs.

Since the Golden Retriever was developed as a water dog, puppies have an incurable affinity to water.

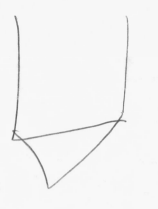

narian to recommend an acceptable maintenance diet. Major dog food manufacturers specialize in this type of food, and it is necessary for you to select the one best suited to your dog's needs. Active dogs may have different requirements than sedate dogs. A Golden Retriever is fully mature around 12 months of age, though it often takes another 12 to 18 months for dog to reach its peak as a performance animal.

Discuss the diet of your active Golden Retriever with your veterinarian or breeder. Some dogs require more food to maintain their weight than others. Also discuss supplementing your Golden's diet with fresh foods with your breeder. Every dog welcomes fresh meat in his diet, and most dogs show an interest in vegetables as well. Experiment to see what your Golden likes. Provided you don't overdo these supplements, you will be adding to your dog's nutrition. You

so may wish to discuss vitamin nd mineral supplements with our breeder, which may or may ot be of value to your dog. A good arometer for the quality of your og's food comes from the other nd of the dog. If your dog's stool eem loose or excessive, the food e's eating is likely more filler than neat. Since Goldens are prone to loat, it's advised that you test your og's food before choosing a brand. Most manufacturers are happy to provide you with a sample of their brand. Place a few pieces of the dry food into a glass of water. If the food swells to five or six times its original size, it is not recommended for the Golden. This is how the food will react in your dog's stomach, and that is not acceptable in a deep-chest breed that is prone to bloat.

Clean water should be available to all dogs. Golden Retriever puppies would often rather swim in water than drink it!

GRAIN-BASED DIETS

Some less expensive dog foods are based on grains and other plant proteins. While these products may appear to be attractively priced, many breeders prefer a diet based on animal proteins and believe that they are more conducive to your dog's health. Many grain-based diets rely on soy protein, which may cause flatulence (passing gas).

There are many cases, however, when your dog might require a special diet. These special requirements should only be recommended by your veterinarian.

As your Golden Retriever matures, his dietary needs change. Active working dogs will require a different nutritional base than will ordinary house dogs.

Since the Golden Retriever was developed as a water dog, puppies have an incurable affinity to water.

SENIOR DIETS

As dogs get older, their metabolism changes. The older dog usually exercises less, moves more slowly and sleeps more. This change in lifestyle and physiological performance requires a change in diet. Since these changes take place slowly, they might not be recognizable. What is easily recognizable is weight gain. By continually feeding your dog an adult maintenance diet when it is slowing down metabolically, your dog will gain weight. Obesity in an older dog compounds the health problems that already accompany old age.

PHOTO BY KENT AND DONNA DANNEN

FEEDING TIPS

Dog food must be at room temperature, neither too hot nor too cold. Fresh water, changed daily and served in a clean bowl, is mandatory, especially when feeding dry food.

Never feed your dog from the table while you are eating. Never feed your dog left-overs from your own meal. They usually contain too much fat and seasoning. The normal food is usually balanced, and adding something extra destroys the balance.

Dogs must chew their food. Hard pellets are excellent; soups and stews are to be avoided.

Except for age-related changes, dogs do not require dietary variations. They can be fed the same diet, day after day, without their becoming bored or ill. Experiment with different flavors featured by the manufacturer.

As your dog gets older, few of his organs function up to par. The kidneys slow down and the intestines become less efficient. These age-related factors are best handled with a change in diet and a change in feeding schedule to give smaller portions that are more easily digested.

There is no single best diet for every older dog. While many dogs do well on light or senior diets,

Exercise is required for your Golden Retriever's mental and physical well-being. It's great for the owner's good health, too.

Nothing compares to a run on the beach for an adult Golden!

If you play ball with a Golden Retriever, be sure the ball is large and tough enough that your dog cannot destroy or swallow it.

clean fresh water at all times. Make sure that the dog's water bowl is clean, and change the water often.

EXERCISE

All dogs require some form of exercise, regardless of breed. A sedentary lifestyle is as harmful to a dog as it is to a person. The Golden Retriever is a sporting dog with an abundance of energy and enthusiasm. Regular walks, play sessions in the yard, or letting the dog run free in the yard under your supervision are all sufficient forms of exercise for the Golden Retriever. For those who are more ambitious, you will find that your adult Golden Retriever will be able to keep up with you on extra long walks or the morning run. Not only

other dogs do better on puppy diets or other special premium diets such as lamb and rice. Be sensitive to your senior Golden Retriever's diet and this will help control other problems that may arise with your old friend.

WATER

Just as your dog needs proper nutrition from his food, water is an essential "nutrient" as well. Water keeps the dog's body properly hydrated and promotes normal function of the body's systems. During housebreaking it is necessary to keep an eye on how much water your Golden Retriever is drinking, but once he is reliably trained he should have access to

GROOMING EQUIPMENT

How much grooming equipment you purchase will depend on how much grooming you are going to do. Here are some basics:

- Natural bristle brush
- Slicker brush
- Metal comb
- Scissors
- Blowdryer
- Rubber mat
- Dog shampoo
- Spray hose attachment
- Ear cleaner
- Cotton balls
- Towels
- Nail clippers

is exercise essential to keep the dog's body fit, it is essential to his mental well-being. A bored dog will find something to do, which often manifests itself in some type of destructive behavior. In this sense, it is essential for the owner's mental well-being as well!

GROOMING

BRUSHING

The luxurious Golden coat is both a bane and a blessing. Lovely to look at, yes, but frequent grooming is required to keep it healthy and attractive. Twice-weekly brushing sessions are a must if you hope to control casting coat (shedding) and keep those silky strands from floating onto your furniture and into your salad bowl. Casting coat is most troublesome in spring and again in fall when the Golden sheds its downy undercoat to

prepare for the changing season. That often surprises a new owner who is not prepared for clouds of dog down rolling across the floors and carpets.

BATHING

Dogs do not need to be bathed as often as humans, but regular bathing is essential for healthy skin and a healthy, shiny coat. Again, like most anything, if you accustom your pup to being bathed as a puppy, it will be second nature by the time he grows up. You want your dog to be at ease in the bath or else it could end up a wet, soapy, messy ordeal for both of you!

Brush your Golden Retriever thoroughly before wetting his coat. This will get rid of most mats and tangles, which are harder to remove when the coat is wet. Make

Before bathing your Golden Retriever, use a natural bristle brush to reach through the top coat.

A Golden should be groomed daily, but a minimum schedule is twice-weekly intense brushing and combing. Use a metal comb to untangle knots.

Your local pet shop will undoubtedly have many types of grooming tools from which to choose.

THE WASH CYCLE...

The use of human soap products like shampoo, bubble bath and hand soap can be damaging to a dog's coat and skin. Human products are too strong and remove the protective oils coating the dog's hair and skin (that make him water-resistant). Use only shampoo made especially for dogs and you may like to use a medicated shampoo which will always help to keep external parasites at bay.

sure that your dog has a good non-slip surface to stand on. Begin by wetting the dog's coat. A shower or hose attachment is necessary for thoroughly wetting and rinsing the coat. Check the water temperature to make sure that it is neither too hot nor too cold.

Next, apply shampoo to the dog's coat and work it into a good lather. You should purchase a shampoo that is made for dogs. Do

Since Goldens love the water, they are easily bathed in a small pool outdoors when the weather permits.

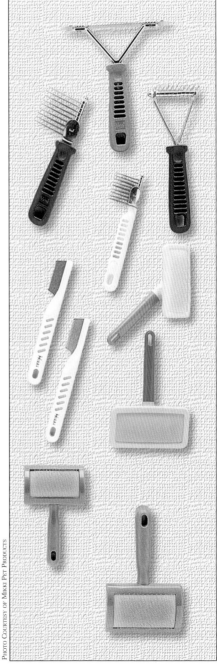

not use a product made for human hair. Wash the head last; you do not want shampoo to drip into the dog's eyes while you are washing the rest of his body. Work the shampoo all the way down to the skin. You can use this opportunity to check the skin for any bumps, bites or other abnormalities. Do not neglect any area of the body— get all of the hard-to-reach places.

Once the dog has been thoroughly shampooed, he requires an equally thorough rinsing. Shampoo left in the coat can be irritating to the skin. Protect his eyes from the shampoo by shielding them with your hand and directing the flow of water in the opposite direction. You should also avoid getting water in the ear canal. Be prepared for your Golden to shake out his coat—you might want to stand back, but make sure you have a hold on the dog to keep him from running through the house.

EAR CLEANING
The ears should be kept clean and any excess hair inside the ear should be trimmed. Ears can be cleaned with cotton wipes and special cleaner or ear powder made especially for dogs. Be on the lookout for any signs of infection or ear-mite infestation. If your Golden Retriever has been shaking his head or scratching at his ears frequently, this usually indicates a problem. If his ears have an unusual odor, this is a sure sign of mite infestation or

If you have a swimming pool, you will have to train your Golden how to enter and exit properly. Goldens love to take a dip on their own, but you must keep a close eye on them.

THE DRY CYCLE...
Once you are sure that the dog is thoroughly rinsed, squeeze the excess water out of the coat with your hand and dry him with a heavy towel. You may choose to use a blowdryer on his coat or just let it dry naturally. In cold weather, never allow your dog outside with a wet coat.

There are "dry bath" products on the market, which are sprays and powders intended for spot cleaning, that can be used between regular baths, if necessary. They are not substitutes for regular baths, but they are easy to use for touch-ups as they do not require rinsing.

infection, and a signal to have his ears checked by the veterinarian.

NAIL CLIPPING

Your Golden Retriever should be accustomed to having his nails trimmed at an early age, since it will be part of your maintenance routine throughout his life. Not only does it look nicer, but a dog with long nails can cause injury if he jumps up or if he scratches someone unintentionally. Also, a long nail has a better chance of ripping and bleeding, or causing the feet to spread. A good rule of thumb is that if you can hear your dog's nails' clicking on the floor when he walks, his nails are too long.

Before you start cutting, make sure you can identify the "quick" in each nail. The quick is a blood vessel that runs through the center of each nail and grows rather close to the end. It will bleed if accidentally cut, which will be quite painful for the dog as it contains nerve endings. Keep some type of

You should trim your Golden's nails carefully so that you don't cut the quick. Clip a little at a time to avoid the possibility of hurting the dog, especially in dark nails where the quick is hard to see.

PEDICURE TIP

A dog that spends a lot of time outside on a hard surface such as cement or pavement will have his nails naturally worn down and may not need to have them trimmed as often, except maybe in the colder months when he is not outside as much. Regardless, it is best to get your dog accustomed to this procedure at an early age so that he is used to it. Some dogs are especially sensitive about having their feet touched, but if a dog has experienced it since he was young, he should not be bothered by it.

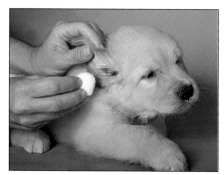

Your Golden puppy's ears should be cleaned weekly with a cotton ball or specially made wipes for ear cleaning.

clotting agent on hand, such as a styptic pencil or styptic powder (the type used for shaving). This will stop the bleeding quickly when applied to the end of the cut nail. Do not panic if this happens, just stop the bleeding and talk soothingly to your dog. Once he has calmed down, move on to the next nail. It is better to clip a little at a time, particularly with black-nailed dogs.

Hold your pup steady as you begin trimming his nails; you do not want him to make any sudden movements or run away. Talk to him soothingly and stroke his fur as you clip. Holding his foot in your hand, simply take off the end of each nail in one quick clip. You can purchase nail clippers that are specially made for dogs; you can

probably find them wherever you buy pet or grooming supplies.

**TRAVELING
WITH YOUR DOG**

CAR TRAVEL
You should accustom your Golden Retriever to riding in a car at an early age. You may or may not take him in the car often, but at the very least he will need to go to the vet and you do not want these trips to be traumatic for the dog or a big hassle for you. The safest way for a dog to ride in the car is in his crate. If he uses a fiberglass crate in the house, you can use the same crate for travel. Wire crates can be used for travel, but fiberglass or wooden crates are safer.

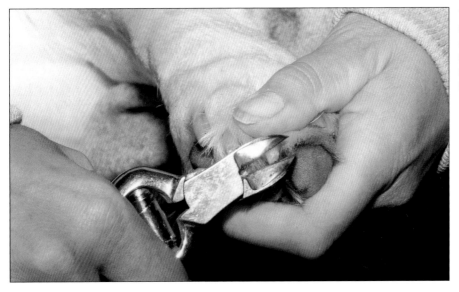

There are many types of nail clippers available at your local pet shop for clipping the Golden's nails.

Your Golden should never be loose in the car when you are driving. For long-distance trips, a large crate in the back of the vehicle is the safest option.

Put the pup in the crate and see how he reacts. If he seems uneasy, you can have a passenger hold him on his lap while you drive. Another option is a specially made safety harness for dogs, which straps the dog in much like a seat belt. Do not let the dog roam loose in the vehicle—this is very dangerous! If you should stop short, your dog can be thrown and injured. If the dog starts climbing on you and pestering you while you are

driving, you will not be able to concentrate on the road. It is an unsafe situation for everyone—human and canine.

For long trips, be prepared to stop to let the dog relieve himself. Bring along whatever you need to clean up after him. You should bring along some old towels and rags, should he have a "bathroom" accident in the car or become carsick.

AIR TRAVEL

If bringing your dog on a flight, you will have to contact the airline to make special arrangements. It is rather common for dogs to travel by air, so major airlines have policies and procedures for pet travel. The dog will be required to travel in an airline-approved crate; you may be able to use your own or the airline can usually supply one at extra cost. To help the dog be at ease, put one of his favorite toys in the crate with him. Do not feed the dog for several hours before the trip to minimize his need to relieve himself. However, you must certify that the dog has been given food and water within a certain time frame of check-in.

Make sure your dog is properly identified and that your contact information appears on his ID tags and on his crate. Check with the airline for specific labeling requirements. Except for very small pets that are allowed in the cabin in their

TRAVELING SAFELY

The most extensive travel you do with your dog may be limited to trips to the veterinarian's office—or you may decide to bring him along for long distances when the family goes on vacation. Whichever the case, it is important to consider your dog's safety while traveling.

TRAVEL TIP
When traveling, never let your dog off-lead in a strange area. Your dog could run away out of fear, decide to chase a passing squirrel or cat or simply want to stretch his legs without restriction—and you might never see your canine friend again.

dations ahead of time anyway, but this is especially important when traveling with a dog. You do not want to make an overnight stop at the only place around for miles and find out that they do not allow dogs. Also, you do not want to reserve a place for your family without confirming that you are traveling with a dog because if it is against their policy you may not have a place to stay.

Alternatively, if you are traveling and choose not to bring

Don't forget to give your Golden time to stretch his legs (on lead, of course) when traveling.

crates, animals travel in a different area of the plane than human passengers, and, although transporting animals is routine for large airlines, there is always the risk of getting separated from your dog. Check with the airline for additional rules regarding crates, food, etc., and follow them carefully.

VACATIONS AND BOARDING
So you want to take a family vacation—and you want to include *all* members of the family. You would probably make arrangements for accommo-

If you cannot take your dog with you on vacation, you should locate a suitable kennel in your area to ensure that your dog is in good hands while you travel.

COLLAR REQUIRED

If your dog gets lost, he is not able to ask for directions home. Identification tags fastened to the collar give important information—the dog's name, the owner's name, the owner's address and a telephone number where the owner can be reached. This makes it easy for whoever finds the dog to contact the owner and arrange to have the dog returned. An added advantage is that a person will be more likely to approach a lost dog who has ID tags on his collar; it tells the person that this is somebody's pet rather than a stray. This is the easiest and fastest method of identification provided that the tags stay on the collar and the collar stays on the dog.

your Golden Retriever, you will have to make arrangements for him while you are away. Some options are to bring him to a neighbor's house to stay while you are gone, to have a trusted neighbor stop by often or stay at your house, or to bring your dog to a reputable boarding kennel. If you choose to board him at a kennel, you should stop by to see the facility and where the dogs are kept to make sure that it is clean. Talk to some of the employees and see how they treat the dogs—do they spend time with the dogs, play with them, exercise them, etc.? You know that your Golden Retriever will not be happy unless he gets regular activity and

Be certain that your Golden's collar fits properly and that his identification tags are attached securely.

IDENTIFICATION OPTIONS

As puppies become more and more expensive, especially those puppies of high quality for showing and/or breeding, they have a greater chance of being stolen. The usual collar dog tag is, of course, easily removed. But there are two techniques that have become widely utilized for identification.

The puppy microchip implantation involves the injection of a small microchip, about the size of a corn kernel, under the skin of the dog. If your dog shows up at a clinic or shelter, or is offered for resale under less than savory circumstances, it can be positively identified by the microchip. The microchip is scanned and a registry quickly identifies you as the owner. This is not only protection against theft, but should the dog run away or go chasing a squirrel and get lost, you have a fair chance of getting it back.

Tattooing is done on various parts of the dog, from his belly to his ears. The number tattooed can be your telephone number or the dog's registration number. When professional dog thieves see a tattooed dog, they usually lose interest in it. For the safety of our dogs, no laboratory facility or dog broker will accept a tattooed dog as stock. Both microchipping and tattooing can be done at your local veterinary clinic.

attention. Also find out the kennel's policy on vaccinations and what they require. This is for all of the dogs' safety, since when dogs are kept together, there is a greater risk of diseases being passed from dog to dog. Many veterinarians offer boarding facilities; this is another option.

IDENTIFICATION

Your Golden Retriever is your valued companion and friend. That is why you always keep a close eye on him and you have made sure that he cannot escape from your property or wriggle out of his collar and run away from you. However, accidents can happen and there may come a time when your dog unexpectedly gets separated from you. If this unfortunate event should occur, the first thing on your mind will be finding him. Proper identification, including an ID tag, a tattoo, and possibly a microchip, will increase the chances of his being returned to you safely and quickly.

Golden Retrievers love the water and are not afraid to jump, even from heights. Hunting dogs develop true style and talent in their "diving" patterns.

PHOTO BY KENT AND DONNA DANNEN

Your Golden Retriever puppy is a blank canvas. Everything he becomes is dependent on the education, patience and energy of his owner.

Living with an untrained dog is a lot like owning a piano that you do not know how to play—it is a nice object to look at, but it does not do much more than that to bring you pleasure. Now try taking piano lessons, and suddenly the piano comes alive and brings forth magical sounds and rhythms that set your heart singing and your body swaying.

The same is true with your Golden Retriever. At first you enjoy seeing him around the house. He does not do much with you except eat, drink and exercise. Come to think of it, he does not bring you much joy, either. He is a big responsibility with a very small return. Often he develops unacceptable behaviors that annoy and/or infuriate you to say nothing of bad habits that may end up costing you great sums of money. Not a good thing!

Now train your Golden Retriever. Enroll in an obedience class. Teach him good manners as you learn how and why he behaves the way he does. Find out how to communicate with your dog and how to recognize and understand his communications

with you. Suddenly the dog takes on a new role in your life—he is smart, interesting, well behaved and fun to be with. He demonstrates his bond of devotion to you daily. In other words, your Golden Retriever does wonders for your ego because he constantly reminds you that you are not only his leader, you are his hero! Miraculous things have happened—you have a wonderful dog (even your family and friends have noticed the transformation!) and you feel good about yourself.

Those involved with teaching

You are personally and solely responsible for molding and training your Golden Retriever puppy. Are you ready for this responsibility?

Training the Golden puppy should involve the whole family. Every member of the family must understand what is expected of the puppy and how to instruct him.

dog obedience and counseling owners about their dogs' behavior have discovered some interesting facts about dog ownership. For example, training dogs when they are puppies results in the highest rate of success in developing well-mannered and well-adjusted adult dogs. Training an older dog, from six months to six years of age, can produce almost equal results, providing that the owner accepts the dog's slower rate of learning capability and is willing to work patiently to help the dog succeed at developing to his fullest potential. Unfortunately, many owners of untrained adult dogs lack the patience factor, so they do not persist until their dogs are successful at learning particular behaviors.

Training a puppy, aged 8 to 16 weeks (20 weeks at the most), is like working with a dry sponge in a pool of water. The pup soaks up whatever you show him and constantly looks for more things to do and learn. At this early age, his body is not yet producing hormones, and therein lies the reason for such a high rate of success. Without hormones, he is focused on his owners and not particularly interested in investigating other places, dogs, people, etc. You are his leader: his provider of food, water, shelter and security. He latches onto you and wants to stay close. He will usually follow you from room to room, will not let you out of his sight when you are outdoors with him, and will respond in like manner to the people and animals you encounter. If you greet a friend warmly, he will be happy to greet the person as well. If, however, you are hesitant or anxious about the approach of a stranger, he will respond accordingly.

Once the puppy begins to produce hormones, his natural curiosity emerges and he begins to investigate the world around him. It is at this time when you may notice that the untrained dog begins to wander away from you and even ignore your commands

HONORABLE MENTION
Dogs are the most honorable animals in existence. They consider another species (humans) as their own. They interface with you. You are their leader. Puppies perceive children to be on their level: their actions around small children are different than their behavior around their adult masters.

OBEDIENCE SCHOOL

Taking your dog to an obedience school may be the best investment in time and money you can ever make. You will enjoy the benefits for the lifetime of your dog and you will have the opportunity to meet people with similar expectations for their companion dogs.

to stay close. When this behavior becomes a problem, the owner has two choices: get rid of the dog or train him. It is strongly urged that you choose the latter option.

Occasionally there are no classes available within a reasonable distance from the owner's home. Sometimes there are classes available but the tuition is too costly. Whatever the circumstances, the solution to training your Golden without obedience classes lies within the pages of this book.

This chapter is devoted to helping you train your Golden Retriever at home. If the recommended procedures are followed faithfully, you may expect positive results that will prove rewarding to both you and your dog.

Whether your new charge is a puppy or a mature adult, the methods of teaching and the

Golden Retriever puppies possess great willingness to please the humans who surround them. It is easier to train a puppy that has been loved and socialized.

Bonding with a puppy has many benefits. Goldens would rather play with a human (you!) than with other dogs. Take full advantage of this trait.

techniques we use in training basic behaviors are the same. After all, no dog, whether puppy or adult, likes harsh or inhumane methods. All creatures, however, respond favorably to gentle motivational methods and sincere praise and encouragement.

HOUSEBREAKING

You can train a puppy to relieve itself wherever you choose. For example, city dwellers often train their puppies to relieve themselves in the gutter because large plots of grass are not readily available. Suburbanites, on the other hand, usually have yards to accommodate their dogs' needs. Outdoor training includes such surfaces as grass, dirt and cement. Indoor training usually means training your dog to newspaper, although this is not recommended with a large dog like the Golden.

When deciding on the surface and location that you will want your Golden Retriever to use, be sure it is going to be permanent. Training your dog to grass and then changing your mind two months later is extremely difficult for both dog and owner.

Next, choose the command you will use each and every time you want your puppy to void. "Go hurry up" and "Go make" are examples of commands commonly used by dog owners. Get in the habit of asking the puppy, "Do you want to go hurry up?" (or whatever your chosen relief command is) before you take him out. That way, when he becomes an adult, you will be able to determine if he wants to

TAKE THE LEAD

Do not carry your dog to his relief area. Lead him there on a leash or, better yet, encourage him to follow you to the spot. If you start carrying him to his spot, you might end up doing this routine forever and your dog will have the satisfaction of having trained *you*.

go out when you ask him. A confirmation will be signs of interest, wagging his tail, watching you intently, going to the door, etc.

PUPPY'S NEEDS
Puppy needs to relieve himself after play periods, after each meal, after he has been sleeping and any time he indicates that he is looking for a place to urinate or defecate.

The urinary and intestinal tract muscles of very young puppies are not fully developed. Therefore, like human babies, puppies need to relieve themselves frequently.

Take your puppy out often—every hour for an eight-week-old, for example. The older the puppy, the less often he will need to relieve himself. Finally, as a mature healthy adult, he will require only three to five relief trips per day.

HOUSING
Since the types of housing and control you provide for your puppy have a direct relationship on the success of housetraining, we consider the various aspects of both before we begin training. Bringing a new puppy home and turning him loose in your house can be compared to turning a child loose in a sports arena and telling the child that the place is all his! The sheer enormity of the

Housebreaking can begin at the breeder's home. A Golden puppy quickly learns the texture of his relief area and will continue to search for it when the time comes. Your breeder can advise you on how to complete the process.

place would be too much for him to handle.

Instead, offer the puppy clearly defined areas where he can play, sleep, eat and live. A room of the house where the family gathers is the most obvious choice. Puppies are social animals

CALM DOWN
Dogs will do anything for your attention. If you reward the dog when he is calm and attentive, you will develop a well-mannered dog. If, on the other hand, you greet your dog excitedly and encourage him to wrestle and roughhouse with you, the dog will greet you the same way and you will have a hyper dog on your hands.

It's advisable to walk the puppy to his designated area on a lead. A puppy will do his best to tell you when it's time to go out. It's up to you to recognize his body language.

KEY TO SUCCESS

Most of all, be consistent. Always take your dog to the same location, always use the same command, and always have him on lead when he is in his relief area, unless a fenced-in yard is available.

By following the Success Method, your puppy will be completely housetrained by the time his muscle and brain development reach maturity. Keep in mind that small breeds usually mature faster than large breeds, but all puppies should be trained by six months of age.

and need to feel a part of the pack right from the start. Hearing your voice, watching you while you are doing things and smelling you nearby are all positive reinforcers that he is now a member of your pack. Usually a family room, the kitchen or a nearby adjoining breakfast nook is ideal for providing safety and security for both puppy and owner.

Within that room there should be a smaller area that the puppy can call his own. A cubbyhole, a wire or fiberglass dog crate or a fenced (not boarded!) corner from which he can view the activities of his new family will be fine. The size of the area or crate is the key factor here. The area must be large enough for the puppy to lie down and stretch out as well as stand up without rubbing his head on the top, yet small enough so that he cannot relieve himself at one end and sleep at the other without coming into contact with his droppings.

Dogs are, by nature, clean animals and will not remain close to their relief areas unless forced to do so. In those cases, they then become dirty dogs and usually remain that way for life.

The crate or cubby should be lined with a clean towel and offer one toy, no more. Do not put food or water in the crate, as eating and drinking will activate the pup's digestive processes and ultimately defeat your purpose

as well as make the puppy very uncomfortable as he attempts to "hold it."

CONTROL

By *control*, we mean helping the puppy to create a lifestyle pattern that will be compatible to that of his human pack *(you!).* Just as we guide little children to learn our way of life, we must show the puppy when it is time to play, eat, sleep, exercise and even entertain himself.

Your puppy should always sleep in his crate. He should also learn that, during times of household confusion and excessive human activity, such as at breakfast when family members are preparing for the day, he can play by himself in relative safety and comfort in his crate. Each time you leave the puppy alone, he should be crated. Puppies are chewers. They cannot tell the difference between lamp cords, television wires, shoes, table legs, etc. Chewing into a television wire, for example, can be fatal to the puppy, while a shorted wire can start a fire in the house.

If the puppy chews on the arm of the chair when he is alone, you will probably discipline him angrily when you get home. Thus, he makes the association that your coming home means he is going to be scolded or punished. (He will

not remember chewing up the chair and is incapable of making the association of the discipline with his naughty deed.)

Other times of excitement, such as family parties, etc., can be fun for the puppy, providing that he can view the activities from the security of his crate. He is not underfoot and he is not being fed all sorts of tidbits that will probably cause him stomach distress, yet he still feels a part of the fun.

SCHEDULE

A puppy should be taken to his relief area each time he is released from his crate, after meals, after a play session, when he first awakens in the morning (at age eight weeks, this

THE CLEAN LIFE

By providing sleeping and resting quarters that fit the dog, and offering frequent opportunities to relieve himself outside his quarters, the puppy quickly learns that the outdoors (or the newspaper if you are training him to paper) is the place to go when he needs to urinate or defecate. It also reinforces his innate desire to keep his sleeping quarters clean. This, in turn, helps develop the muscle control that will eventually produce a dog with clean living habits.

A fenced yard or large secure enclosure is ideal for giving Goldens safe off-lead exercise.

POTTY TIPS

When housebreaking your puppy, restrict water intake after evening meals. Offer a few licks at a time—never let a young puppy gulp water after meals.

Never line your pup's sleeping area with newspaper. Puppy litters are usually raised on newspaper and, once in your home, the puppy will immediately associate newspaper with voiding. Never put newspaper on any floor while housetraining, as this will only confuse the puppy.

can mean 5 a.m.!). The puppy will indicate that he's ready "to go" by circling or sniffing busily—do not misinterpret these signs. For a puppy less than ten weeks of age, a routine of taking him out every hour is necessary. As the puppy grows, he will be able to wait for longer periods of time.

Keep trips to his relief area short. Stay no more than five or six minutes and then return to the house. If he goes during that time, praise him lavishly and take him indoors immediately. If he does not, but he has an accident when you go back indoors, pick him up immediately, say "No! No!" and return to his relief area. Wait a few minutes, then return to the house again. Never hit a puppy or put his face in urine or excrement

Canine Development Schedule

It is important to understand how and at what age a puppy develops into adulthood.
If you are a puppy owner, consult the following Canine Development Schedule to determine
the stage of development your Golden Retriever puppy is currently experiencing.
This knowledge will help you as you work with the puppy in the weeks and months ahead.

Period	Age	Characteristics
FIRST TO THIRD	BIRTH TO SEVEN WEEKS	Puppy needs food, sleep and warmth, and responds to simple and gentle touching. Needs mother for security and disciplining. Needs littermates for learning and interacting with other dogs. Pup learns to function within a pack and learns pack order of dominance. Begin socializing with adults and children for short periods. Begins to become aware of his environment.
FOURTH	EIGHT TO TWELVE WEEKS	Brain is fully developed. Needs socializing with outside world. Remove from mother and littermates. Needs to change from canine pack to human pack. Human dominance necessary. Fear period occurs between 8 and 16 weeks. Avoid fright and pain.
FIFTH	THIRTEEN TO SIXTEEN WEEKS	Training and formal obedience should begin. Less association with other dogs, more with people, places, situations. Period will pass easily if you remember this is pup's change-to-adolescence time. Be firm and fair. Flight instinct prominent. Permissiveness and over-disciplining can do permanent damage. Praise for good behavior.
JUVENILE	FOUR TO EIGHT MONTHS	Another fear period about 7 to 8 months of age. It passes quickly, but be cautious of fright and pain. Sexual maturity reached. Dominant traits established. Dog should understand sit, down, come and stay by now.

NOTE: THESE ARE APPROXIMATE TIME FRAMES. ALLOW FOR INDIVIDUAL DIFFERENCES IN PUPPIES.

when he has an accident!

Once indoors, put the puppy in his crate until you have had time to clean up his accident. Then release him to the family area and watch him more closely than before. Chances are, his accident was a result of your not picking up his signal or waiting too long before offering him the opportunity to relieve himself. Never hold a grudge against the puppy for accidents.

Let the puppy learn that going outdoors means it is time to relieve himself, not play. Once trained, he will be able to play indoors and out and still differentiate between the times for play versus the times for relief.

Help him develop regular hours for naps, being alone, playing by himself and just resting, all in his crate. Encourage him to entertain himself while you are busy with your activities.

Let him learn that having you near is comforting, but it is not your only purpose in life to provide him with undivided attention.

Each time you put a puppy in his crate, tell him, "Crate time!" (or whatever command you choose). Soon, he will run to his crate when he hears you say those words.

In the beginning of his training, do not leave him in his crate for prolonged periods of time except during the night when everyone is sleeping. Make his experience with his crate a pleasant one and, as an adult, he will love his crate and willingly stay in it for several hours. There are millions of people who go to work every day and leave their adult dogs crated while they are away. The dogs accept this as their lifestyle and look forward to "crate time."

Crate training provides safety for you, the puppy and the home. It also provides the puppy with a feeling of security, and that helps the puppy achieve self-confidence and clean habits.

HOW MANY TIMES A DAY?

AGE	RELIEF TRIPS
To 14 weeks	10
14–22 weeks	8
22–32 weeks	6
Adulthood	4
(dog stops growing)	

These are estimates, of course, but they are a guide to the *minimum* opportunities a dog should have each day to relieve itself.

Remember that one of the primary ingredients in housetraining your puppy is control. Regardless of your lifestyle, there will always be occasions when you will need to have a place where your dog can stay and be happy and safe. Crate training is the answer for now and in the future.

In conclusion, a few key elements are really all you need for a successful house- and crate-training method—consistency, frequency, praise, control and supervision. By following these procedures with a normal, healthy puppy, you and the puppy will soon be past the stage of "accidents" and ready to move on to a full and rewarding life together.

KEEP THE "PUPPY" IN YOUR PUPPY

Before we discuss the roles of discipline in training, let us take a time-out for a discussion of fun and play in your puppy's schedule. As canines, Goldens are social animals and thrive on play and interaction with their masters (and other dogs, too). Exercising and playing with your Golden Retriever puppy help to burn some of his gundog fuel and gives the dog focus. Trying to obedience-train a Golden who is hyper and wound-up is practically impossible. Further, a play-deprived Golden can become

destructive as he tries to find ways to release his pent-up energy.

Outline a schedule of activities for your blossoming Golden pup that includes canine-human games as well as safe doggy exercises. The word "retriever" is not in the Golden's name for nothing! Puppy catch is a great way of occupying the Golden, who is content to fetch a ball or flying disk for hours (if you have the time!). The author doesn't advise games of chasing because it can imprint on the Golden that it is okay to run away from his master. Likewise, tug-of-war is not advised as this dominance game can give the puppy the impression that he can climb to the top of the heap and become "top dog." The role of top dog is always reserved for his master and trainer.

All work and no play makes your Golden an unhappy, unfocused pup.

MEALTIME

Mealtime should be a peaceful time for your puppy. Do not put his food and water bowls in a high-traffic area in the house. For example, give him his own little corner of the kitchen where he can eat undisturbed and where he will not be underfoot. Do not allow small children or other family members to disrupt the pup when he is eating.

Ideally your Golden puppy will find and mark a place that he will always use to relieve himself. If there is an area of your yard that you do not want him to use, it's best to deny him access.

PLAN TO PLAY

The puppy should also have regular play and exercise sessions when he is with you or a family member. Exercise for a very young puppy can consist of a short walk around the house or yard. Playing can include fetching games with a large ball or a Frisbee. (All puppies teethe and need soft things upon which to chew.) Remember to restrict play periods to indoors within his living area (the family room, for example) until he is completely housetrained.

Make time for play in your schedule and soon your Golden Retriever and you will be bonding and sharing quality time during training sessions as well.

ROLES OF DISCIPLINE, REWARD AND PUNISHMENT

Discipline, training one to act in accordance with rules, brings order to life. It is as simple as that. Without discipline, particularly in a group society, chaos reigns supreme and the group will eventually perish. Humans and canines are social animals and need some form of discipline in order to function effectively. They must procure food, protect their home base and their young and reproduce to keep the species going.

If there were no discipline in the lives of social animals, they

would eventually die from starvation and/or predation by other stronger animals.

In the case of domestic canines, dogs need discipline in their lives in order to understand how their pack (you and other family members) functions and how they must act in order to survive.

A large humane society in a highly populated area in the US recently surveyed dog owners regarding their satisfaction with

THE SUCCESS METHOD

Success that comes by luck is usually short-lived. Success that comes by well-thought-out proven methods is often more easily achieved and permanent. This is the Success Method. It is designed to give you, the puppy owner, a simple yet proven way to help your puppy develop clean living habits and a feeling of security in his new environment.

6 Steps to Successful Crate Training

1 Tell the puppy "Crate time!" and place him in the crate with a small treat (a piece of cheese or half of a biscuit). Let him stay in the crate for five minutes while you are in the same room. Then release him and praise lavishly. Never release him when he is fussing. Wait until he is quiet before you let him out.

2 Repeat Step 1 several times a day.

3 The next day, place the puppy in the crate as before. Let him stay there for ten minutes. Do this several times.

4 Continue building time in five-minute increments until the puppy stays in his crate for 30 minutes with you in the room. Always take him to his relief area after prolonged periods in his crate.

5 Now go back to Step 1 and let the puppy stay in his crate for five minutes, this time while you are out of the room.

6 Once again, build crate time in five-minute increments with you out of the room. When the puppy will stay willingly in his crate (he may even fall asleep!) for 30 minutes with you out of the room, he will be ready to stay in it for several hours at a time.

their relationships with their dogs. People who had trained their dogs were 75% more satisfied with their pets than those who had never trained their dogs.

Dr. Edward Thorndike, a noted psychologist, established *Thorndike's Theory of Learning*, which states that a behavior that results in a pleasant event tends to be repeated. Likewise, a behavior that results in an unpleasant event tends not to be repeated. It is this theory on which training methods are based today. For example, if you manipulate a dog to perform a specific behavior and reward him for doing it, he is likely to do it again because he enjoyed the end result.

Occasionally, punishment, a penalty inflicted for an offense, is necessary. The best type of punishment often comes from an outside source. For example, a child is told not to touch the stove because he may get burned. He disobeys and touches the stove. In doing so, he receives a burn. From that time on, he respects the heat of the stove and avoids contact with it. Therefore, a behavior that results in an unpleasant event tends not to be repeated.

A good example of a dog learning the hard way is the dog who chases the house cat. He is told many times to leave the cat alone, yet he persists in teasing the cat. Then, one day he begins

GENTLE TEACHING
Golden Retrievers are known to be "soft" dogs who learn best with gentle teaching. A Golden thrives on praise and knowing he has pleased his

person. Never physically abuse your dog or hit him with your hand, foot, newspaper or other object. That will only teach the dog to be afraid of you.

chasing the cat but the cat turns and swipes a claw across the dog's face, leaving him with a painful gash on his nose. The final result is that the dog stops chasing the cat.

TRAINING EQUIPMENT

COLLAR
A simple buckle collar is fine for most dogs. One who pulls too

hard on the leash may require a choke collar. Be cautious with a chain choke collar, as this can damage the Golden's coat around the neck. Only in the most severe cases of a dog's being totally out of control is the use of a pinch collar recommended. However, Goldens *never* should be subjected to such a device.

LEAD
A 1- to 2-yard lead is recommended, preferably made of leather, nylon or heavy cloth. A chain lead is not recommended, as many dog owners find that the chain cuts into their hands and that frequently switching the lead back and forth between their hands is painful.

Within the first few days in your new home, introduce the light lead to the puppy. Do not attach the lead and attempt to drag the puppy around the neighborhood. Simply attach the lead to the collar and let the puppy wander around the house. Supervise him so that he doesn't manage to knock over plant

Dogs need discipline as well as love and companionship.

Make training time fun time, too. The intelligent Golden can easily be taught tricks like "give me your paw."

Choose the Right Collar

The BUCKLE COLLAR is the standard collar used for everyday purpose. Be sure that you adjust the buckle on growing puppies. Check it every day. It can become too tight overnight! These collars can be made of leather or nylon. Attach your dog's identification tags to this collar.

The CHOKE COLLAR is designed for training. It is constructed of highly polished steel so that it slides easily through the stainless steel loop. The idea is that the dog controls the pressure around his neck and he will stop pulling if the collar becomes uncomfortable. *Never* leave a choke collar on your dog when not training.

The HALTER is for a trained dog that has to be restrained to prevent running away, chasing a cat and the like. Considered the most humane of all collars, it is frequently used on smaller dogs for which collars are not comfortable.

stands, small tables or the like. You can play with the puppy while he is trailing the leash behind him. Toss a ball to distract him from the leash, which may be upsetting him. Once he is comfortable with the leash, you can move the game to outside. Within a few days, you can take the end of the lead and walk together around your yard.

TREATS

Have a bag of treats on hand. Something nutritious and easy to swallow works best. Use a soft treat, a chunk of cheese or a piece of cooked chicken rather than a dry biscuit. By the time the dog gets done chewing a dry treat, he will forget why he is being rewarded in the first place! Using food rewards will not teach a dog to beg at the table—the only way to teach a dog to beg at the table is to give him food from the table. In training, rewarding the dog with a food treat will help him associate praise and the treats with learning new behaviors that obviously please his owner.

TRAINING BEGINS: ASK THE DOG A QUESTION

In order to teach your dog anything, you must first get his attention. After all, he cannot learn anything if he is looking away from you with his mind on something else.

To get his attention, ask him

"School?" and immediately walk over to him and give him a treat as you tell him, "Good dog." Wait a minute or two and repeat the routine, this time with a treat in your hand as you approach within a foot of the dog. Do not go directly to him, but stop about a foot short of him and hold out the treat as you ask, "School?" He will see you approaching with a treat in your hand and most likely begin walking toward you. As you meet, give him the treat and praise again.

Your local pet shop usually has a wide variety of leads from which you can make your choice.

The third time, ask the question, have a treat in your hand and walk only a short distance toward the dog so that he must walk almost all the way to you. As he reaches you, give him the treat and praise again.

By this time, the dog will

If your Golden Retriever has received training throughout his life by various members of the family, he will respond positively to both children and adults.

probably be getting the idea that if he pays attention to you, especially when you ask that question, it will pay off in treats and fun activities for him. In other words, he learns that "school" means doing fun things with you that result in treats and positive attention for him.

Remember that the dog does not understand your verbal language, he only recognizes sounds. Your question translates to a series of sounds for him, and those sounds become the signal to go to you and pay attention; if he does, he will get to interact with you plus receive treats and praise.

THE BASIC COMMANDS

Now it is time to apply our positive training methods to actual obedience commands. Do not become disheartened if your Golden doesn't pick up his first lesson or two immediately. Every dog is different, and some dogs learn instantly and others require repetition and patience. Do not give up on a command until the

dog has learned it. Remember to keep lessons upbeat by using a happy, energized voice. Your dog doesn't know the word "sit" or "down" (yet!), but he does recognize your tone of voice. Sometimes in life (and dog training) it's not what you say—it's how you say it. This life mantra applies to training dogs as well.

TEACHING SIT

Now that you have the dog's attention, attach his lead and hold it in your left hand and a food treat in your right. Place your food hand at the dog's nose and let him lick the treat but not take it from

Once your Golden is sufficiently trained, you can practice your commands and incorporate a favorite game into the sessions.

will wean him off of the food treats but still maintain the verbal praise. After all, you will always have your voice with you, and there will be many times when you have no food rewards but expect the dog to obey.

Since most Goldens love to eat, using food rewards is an absolutely fool-proof way to train this breed.

TEACHING DOWN
Teaching the down exercise is easy when you understand how the dog perceives the down position, and it is very difficult when you do not. Dogs perceive the down position as a submissive one, therefore teaching the down exercise using a forceful method can sometimes make the dog develop such a fear of the down that he either runs away when

you. Say "Sit" and slowly raise your food hand from in front of the dog's nose up over his head so that he is looking at the ceiling. As he bends his head upward, he will have to bend his knees to maintain his balance. As he bends his knees, he will assume a sit position. At that point, release the food treat and praise lavishly with comments such as "Good dog! Good sit!", etc. Remember to always praise enthusiastically, because dogs relish verbal praise from their owners and feel so proud of themselves whenever they accomplish a behavior.

You will not use food forever in getting the dog to obey your commands. Food is only used to teach new behaviors, and once the dog knows what you want when you give a specific command, you

PRACTICE MAKES PERFECT
- Have training lessons with your dog every day in several short segments—three to five times a day for a few minutes at a time is ideal.
- Do not have long practice sessions. The dog will become easily bored.
- Never practice when you are tired, ill, worried or in an otherwise negative mood. This will transmit to the dog and may have an adverse effect on its performance.

Think fun, short and above all *positive!* End each session on a high note, rather than a failed exercise, and make sure to give a lot of praise. Enjoy the training and help your dog enjoy it, too.

Shaking hands is among the most common tricks to teach your dog. Goldens are naturally very friendly and happy to lend a paw.

you say "Down" or he attempts to bite the person who tries to force him down.

Have the dog sit close alongside your left leg, facing in the same direction as you are. Hold the lead in your left hand and a food treat in your right. Now place your left hand lightly on the top of the dog's shoulders where they meet above the spinal cord. Do not push down on the dog's shoulders; simply rest your left hand there so you can guide the dog to lie down close to your left leg rather than to swing away

You can train your Golden Retriever to retrieve almost anything! It's better to use a retrieving dummy or a toy than a natural tree branch, which might have been treated with a toxic insecticide.

from your side when he drops.

Now place the food hand at the dog's nose, say "Down" very softly (almost a whisper), and slowly lower the food hand to the dog's front feet. When the food hand reaches the floor, begin moving it forward along the floor in front of the dog. Keep talking softly to the dog, saying things like, "Do you want this treat? You can do this, good dog." Your reassuring tone of voice will help calm the dog as he tries to follow the food hand in order to get the treat.

When the dog's elbows touch the floor, release the food and praise softly. Try to get the dog to maintain that down position for several seconds before you let him sit up again. The goal here is to get the dog to settle down and not feel threatened in the down position.

TEACHING STAY

It is easy to teach the dog to stay in either a sit or a down position. Again, we use food and praise

DOUBLE JEOPARDY

A dog in jeopardy never lies down. He stays alert on his feet because instinct tells him that he may have to run away or fight for his survival. Therefore, if a dog feels threatened or anxious, he will not lie down. Consequently, it is important to have the dog calm and relaxed as he learns the down exercise.

during the teaching process as we help the dog to understand exactly what it is that we are expecting him to do.

To teach the sit/stay, start with the dog sitting on your left side as before and hold the lead in your left hand. Have a food treat in your right hand and place your food hand at the dog's nose. Say "Stay" and step out on your right foot to stand directly in front of the dog, toe to toe, as he licks and nibbles the treat. Be sure to keep his head facing upward to maintain the sit position. Count to five and then swing around to stand next to the dog again with him on your left. As soon as you get back to the original position, release the food and praise lavishly.

To teach the down/stay, do the down as previously described. As soon as the dog lies down, say "Stay" and step out on your right foot just as you did in the sit/stay. Count to five and then return to stand beside the dog with him on your left side. Release the treat and praise as always.

Within a week or ten days, you can begin to add a bit of distance between you and your dog when you leave him. When you do, use your left hand open with the palm facing the dog as a stay signal, much the same as the hand signal a police officer uses to stop traffic at an intersection. Hold the food treat in your right

Teaching a dog to sit/stay is easy when you use food and praise in the training process.

hand as before, but this time the food is not touching the dog's nose. He will watch the food hand and quickly learn that he is going to get that treat as soon as you return to his side.

"WHERE ARE YOU?"

When calling the dog, do not say "Come." Say things like, "Rover, where are you? See if you can find me! I have a cookie for you!" Keep up a constant line of chatter with coaxing sounds and frequent questions such as, "Where are you?" The dog will learn to follow the sound of your voice to locate you and receive his reward.

When you can stand 3 feet away from your dog for 30 seconds, you can then begin building time and distance in both stays. Eventually, the dog can be expected to remain in the stay position for prolonged periods of time until you return to him or call him to you. Always praise lavishly when he stays.

When teaching your Golden to come, never use the word "come."

"COME" . . . BACK

Never call your dog to come to you for a correction or scold him when he reaches you. That is the quickest way to turn a "Come" command into "Go away fast!" Dogs think only in the present tense and he will connect the scolding with coming to his master, not with the misbehavior of a few moments earlier.

TEACHING COME

If you make teaching "come" a fun experience, you should never have a "student" that does not love the game or that fails to come when called. The secret, it seems, is never to teach the word "come."

At times when an owner most wants his dog to come when called, the owner is likely upset or anxious and he allows these feelings to come through in the tone of his voice when he calls his dog. Hearing that desperation in his owner's voice, the dog fears the results of going to him and therefore either disobeys outright or runs in the opposite direction. The secret, therefore, is to teach the dog a game and, when you want him to come to you, simply play the game. It is practically a no-fail solution!

To begin, have several members of your family take a few food treats and each go into a different room in the house. Take turns calling the dog, and each person should celebrate the dog's finding him with a treat and lots of happy praise. When a person calls the dog, he is actually inviting the dog to find him and get a treat as a reward for "winning."

A few turns of the "Where are you?" game and the dog will figure out that everyone is playing the game and that each person has a big celebration awaiting the dog's success at locating them. Once he learns to love the game, simply calling out "Where are you?" will bring him running from wherever he is when he hears that all-important question.

The come command is recognized as one of the most important things to teach a dog, but there are trainers who work with thousands of dogs and never teach the actual word "Come." Yet these dogs will race to respond to a person who uses the dog's name followed by "Where are you?" For example, a woman has a 12-year-old companion dog who went blind, but who never fails to locate her owner when asked, "Where are you?"

Children particularly love to play this game with their dogs. Children can hide in smaller places like a shower or bathtub, behind a bed or under a table. The dog needs to work a little bit harder to find these hiding places, but when he does, he loves to celebrate with a treat and a hug from a favorite youngster.

Your Golden must be trained to heel. He should remain close to your side and anticipate your next command.

TEACHING HEEL

Heeling means that the dog walks beside the owner without pulling. It takes time and patience on the owner's part to succeed at teaching the dog that he (the owner) will not proceed unless the dog is walking calmly beside him. Pulling out ahead on the lead is definitely not acceptable.

Begin with holding the lead in your left hand as the dog sits beside your left leg. Move the loop end of the lead to your right hand but keep your left hand short on the lead so it keeps the dog in close next to you.

Say "Heel" and step forward on your left foot. Keep the dog close to you and take three steps. Stop and have the dog sit next to you in what we now call the "heel position." Praise verbally, but do not touch the dog. Hesitate a moment and begin again with "Heel," taking three steps and stopping, at which point the dog is told to sit again.

Your goal here is to have the dog walk those three steps without pulling on the lead. When he will walk calmly beside you for three steps without pulling, increase the number of steps you take to five. When he will walk politely beside you while you take five steps, you can increase the length of your walk to ten steps. Keep increasing the length of your stroll until the dog will walk quietly beside you without pulling as long as you want him to heel. When you stop heeling, indicate to the dog that the exercise is over by verbally praising as you pet him and say "OK, good dog." The "OK" is used as a release word, meaning that the exercise is finished and the dog is free to relax.

If you are dealing with a dog who insists on pulling you around, simply "put on your

---

HEELING WELL

Teach your dog to heel in an enclosed area. Once you think the dog will obey reliably and you want to attempt advanced obedience exercises such as off-lead heeling, test him in a fenced in area so he cannot run away.

Heel training requires constant repetition and experience. Start the training indoors, if possible, where there are few distractions like other people or vehicles. Goldens make excellent guides for the vision-impaired. This Golden is being trained at The Seeing Eye®, Morristown, NJ.

THINK BEFORE YOU BARK

Dogs are sensitive to their master's moods and emotions. Use your voice wisely when communicating with your dog. Never raise your voice at your dog unless you are angry and trying to correct him. "Barking" at your dog can become as meaningless as "dogspeak" is to you. Think before you bark!

brakes" and stand your ground until the dog realizes that the two of you are not going anywhere until he is beside you and moving at your pace, not his. It may take some time just standing there to convince the dog that you are the leader and you will be the one to decide on the direction and speed of your travel.

Each time the dog looks up at you or slows down to give a slack lead between the two of you, quietly praise him and say, "Good heel. Good dog." Eventually, the dog will begin to respond and within a few days he will be walking politely beside you without pulling on the lead. At first, the training sessions should be kept short and very positive; soon the dog will be able to walk nicely with you for increasingly longer distances. Remember also to give the dog free time and the opportunity to run and play when you are done with heel practice.

WEANING OFF FOOD IN TRAINING

Food is used in training new behaviors. Once the dog understands what behavior goes with a specific command, it is time to start weaning him off the food treats. At first, give a treat after each exercise. Then, start to give a treat only after every other exercise. Mix up the times when you offer a food reward and the times when you only offer praise so that the dog will never know when he is going to receive both

food and praise and when he is going to receive only praise. This is called a variable ratio reward system and it proves successful because there is always the chance that the owner will produce a treat, so the dog never stops trying for that reward. No matter what, *always* give verbal praise.

OBEDIENCE CLASSES

As previously discussed, it is a good idea to enroll in an obedience class if one is available in your area. Many areas have dog clubs that offer basic obedience training as well as preparatory classes for obedience competition. There are also local dog trainers who offer similar classes.

At obedience trials, dogs can earn titles at various levels of competition. The beginning levels of competition include basic behaviors such as sit, down, heel,

OBEDIENCE CLASS

A basic obedience beginner's class usually lasts for six to eight weeks. Dog and owner attend an hour-long lesson once a week and practice for a few minutes, several times a day, each day at home. If done properly, the whole procedure will result in a well-mannered dog and an owner who delights in living with a pet that is eager to please and enjoys doing things with his owner.

etc. The more advanced levels of competition include jumping, retrieving, scent discrimination and signal work. The advanced levels require a dog and owner to put a lot of time and effort into their training and the titles that can be earned at these levels of competition are very prestigious.

OTHER ACTIVITIES FOR LIFE

Whether a dog is trained in the structured environment of a class or alone with his owner at home, there are many fun activities that can bring rewards to both owner and dog once they have mastered basic control.

Teaching the dog to help out around the home, in the yard or on the farm provides great satisfaction to both dog and owner. In addition, the dog's help makes life a little easier for his owner and raises his stature as a valued companion to his family. It helps give the dog a purpose by occupying his mind and providing an outlet for his energy.

Backpacking is an exciting and healthful activity that the dog can be taught without assistance from more than his owner. The exercise of walking and climbing is good for man and dog alike, and the bond that they develop together is priceless.

If you are interested in participating in organized competition with your Golden Retriever, there

Golden Retrievers can accomplish anything they are trained to do. Few breeds have the trainability and adaptability of the Golden. Here's a Golden backpacking on vacation.

are activities other than obedience in which you and your dog can become involved. Agility is a popular and fun sport where dogs run through an obstacle course that includes various jumps, tunnels and other exercises to test the dog's speed and coordination. The owners often run through the course beside their dogs to give commands and to guide them through the course. Although competitive, the focus is on fun— it's fun to do, fun to watch, and great exercise.

A BORN PRODIGY

Occasionally, a dog and owner who have not attended formal classes have been able to earn entry-level titles by obtaining competition rules and regulations from a local kennel club and practicing on their own to a degree of perfection. Obtaining the higher level titles, however, almost always requires extensive training under the tutelage of experienced instructors. In addition, the more difficult levels require more specialized equipment whereas the lower levels do not.

First Aid
at a Glance

Burns
Place the affected area under cool water; use ice if only a small area is burned.

Bee stings/Insect bites
Apply ice to relieve swelling; antihistamine dosed properly.

Animal bites
Clean any bleeding area; apply pressure until bleeding subsides; go to the vet.

Spider bites
Use cold compress and a pressurized pack to inhibit venom's spreading.

Antifreeze poisoning
Immediately induce vomiting by using hydrogen peroxide.

Fish hooks
Removal best handled by vet; hook must be cut in order to remove.

Snake bites
Pack ice around bite; contact vet quickly; identify snake for proper antivenin.

Car accident
Move dog from roadway with blanket; seek veterinary aid.

Shock
Calm the dog, keep him warm; seek immediate veterinary help.

Nosebleed
Apply cold compress to the nose; apply pressure to any visible abrasion.

Bleeding
Apply pressure above the area; treat wound by applying a cotton pack.

Heat stroke
Submerge dog in cold bath; cool down with fresh air and water; go to the vet.

Frostbite/Hypothermia
Warm the dog with a warm bath, electric blankets or hot water bottles.

Abrasions
Clean the wound and wash out thoroughly with fresh water; apply antiseptic.

!! *Remember: an injured dog may attempt to bite a helping hand from fear and confusion. Always muzzle the dog before trying to offer assistance.* !!

GOLDEN RETRIEVER

Dogs suffer from many of the same physical illnesses as people. They might even share many of the same psychological problems. Since people usually know more about human diseases than canine maladies, many of the terms used in this chapter will be familiar but not necessarily those used by veterinarians. We will use the term *X-ray*, instead of the more acceptable term *radiograph*. We will also use the familiar term *symptoms* even though dogs don't have symptoms, which are verbal descriptions of the patient's feelings; dogs have *clinical signs*. Since dogs can't speak, we have to look for clinical signs...but we still use the term *symptoms* in this book.

As a general rule, medicine is *practiced*. That term is not arbitrary. Medicine is a constantly changing art as we learn more and more about genetics, electronic aids (like CAT scans) and daily laboratory advances. There are many dog maladies, like canine hip dysplasia, which are not universally treated in the same manner. Some veterinarians opt for surgery more often than others do.

SELECTING A VETERINARIAN

Your selection of a veterinarian should be based upon both his convenience to your home and his skills with small animals, especially dogs. You want a vet who is close because you might have emergencies or need to make multiple visits for treatments. You want a vet who has services that you might require such as a boarding kennel and grooming facilities, as well as sophisticated pet

Never compromise in your selection of a veterinarian. Find a vet who offers the services you need and with whom you feel comfortable.

supplies and a good reputation for ability and responsiveness. There is nothing more frustrating than having to wait a day or more to get a response from your veterinarian.

All veterinarians are licensed and their diplomas and/or certificates should be displayed in their waiting rooms. There are, however, many veterinary specialties that usually require further studies and internships. There are specialists in heart problems (veterinary cardiologists), skin problems (veterinary dermatolo-

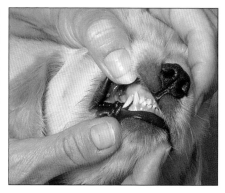

Your Golden Retriever's teeth should be checked regularly by your veterinarian.

gists), teeth and gum problems (veterinary dentists), eye problems (veterinary ophthalmologists) and X-rays (veterinary radiologists), and surgeons who have specialties in bones, muscles or other organs. Most veterinarians do routine surgery such as neutering, stitching up wounds and docking tails for those breeds in which such is required for show purposes. When the problem affecting your dog is serious, it is not unusual or impudent to get another medical opinion. You might also want to compare costs among

several veterinarians. Sophisticated health care and veterinary services can be very costly. Don't be bashful about discussing these costs with your veterinarian or his staff. If several treatment options are available, cost may play a role in deciding which route to take.

PREVENTATIVE MEDICINE
It is much easier, less costly and more effective to practice preventative medicine than to fight bouts of illness and disease. Properly bred puppies come from parents that were selected based upon their genetic disease profile. Their mothers should have been vaccinated, free of all internal and external parasites, and properly nourished. For these reasons, a visit to the veterinarian who cared for the dam (mother) is recommended. The dam can pass on disease resistance to her puppies, which can last for eight to ten weeks. She can also pass on parasites and many infections. That's why you should visit the veterinarian who cared for the dam.

WEANING TO FIVE MONTHS OLD
Puppies should be weaned by the time they are about two months old. A puppy that remains for at least eight weeks with his mother and littermates usually adapts better to other

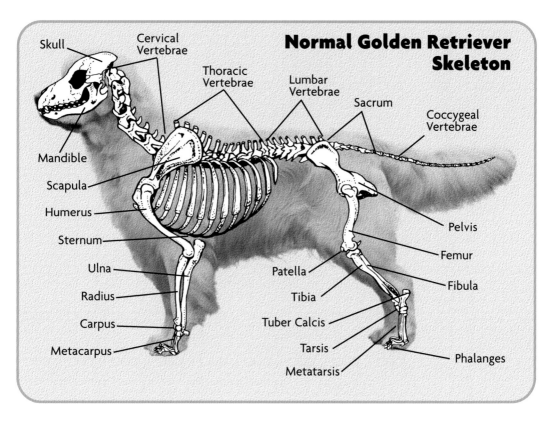

Normal Golden Retriever Skeleton

Skull
Cervical Vertebrae
Thoracic Vertebrae
Lumbar Vertebrae
Sacrum
Coccygeal Vertebrae
Mandible
Scapula
Humerus
Sternum
Ulna
Radius
Carpus
Metacarpus
Patella
Tibia
Tuber Calcis
Tarsis
Metatarsis
Pelvis
Femur
Fibula
Phalanges

dogs and people later in life.

In every case, you should have your newly acquired puppy examined by a veterinarian immediately. Vaccination programs usually begin when the puppy is very young.

The puppy will have its teeth examined and have its skeletal conformation and general health checked prior to certification by the veterinarian. Many puppies have problems with their kneecaps, cataracts and other eye problems, heart murmurs and undescended testicles. They may also have personality problems and your veterinarian might have training in temperament evaluation.

VACCINATION SCHEDULING
Most vaccinations are given by injection and should only be done by a veterinarian. Both he and you should keep a record of the date of the injection, the identification of the vaccine and the amount given. The first vaccinations should start when

HEALTH AND VACCINATION SCHEDULE

Age in Weeks:	3rd	6th	8th	10th	12th	14th	16th	20-24th
Worm Control	✔	✔	✔	✔	✔	✔	✔	✔
Neutering								✔
Heartworm		✔						✔
Parvovirus		✔	✔		✔			✔
Distemper			✔		✔		✔	
Hepatitis			✔		✔		✔	
Leptospirosis		✔		✔		✔		
Parainfluenza		✔		✔		✔		
Dental Examination			✔					✔
Complete Physical			✔					✔
Temperament Testing			✔					
Coronavirus					✔			
Canine Cough		✔						
Hip Dysplasia								✔
Rabies								✔

Vaccinations are not instantly effective. It takes about two weeks for the dog's immune system to develop antibodies. Most vaccinations require annual booster shots. Your veterinarian should guide you in this regard.

the puppy is 6–8 weeks old, the second when it is 10–12 weeks of age and the third when it is 14–16 weeks of age. Vaccinations should never be given without a two- to three-week lapse between injections.

Most vaccinations immunize your puppy against viruses. The usual vaccines contain immunizing doses of several different viruses such as distemper, parvovirus, parainfluenza and hepatitis. There are other vaccines available when the puppy is at risk. You should rely upon professional advice.

This is especially true for the booster-shot program. Most vaccination programs require a booster when the puppy is a year old and once a year thereafter. In some cases, circumstances may require more frequent immunizations. Canine cough, more formally known as tracheobronchitis, is treated with a vaccine that is sprayed into the dog's nostrils.

The effectiveness of a parvovirus vaccination program can be tested using the parvovirus antibody titer to be certain that the vaccinations are

protective. Your veterinarian will explain and manage all of these details.

FIVE MONTHS TO ONE YEAR OF AGE

By the time your puppy is five months old, he should have completed most of his vaccination program. During his physical examination, he should be evaluated for the common hip dysplasia and other diseases of the joints. There are tests to assist in the prediction of these problems. Other tests can be run to assess the effectiveness of the vaccination program.

Unless you intend to breed or show your dog, neutering/spaying the puppy at the appropriate age is recommended. Discuss this with your veterinarian. By the time your Golden Retriever is around six months of age, he can be seriously evaluated for his conformation to the breed standard, thus determining show potential and desirability as a sire or dam. Of course, desirability as a working-dog sire or dam has less to do with the breed standard than it does training and performance. If the puppy is not top class and therefore is not a candidate for a serious breeding program, most professionals advise neutering the puppy. Neutering has proven to be extremely beneficial to both male and female puppies.

Besides eliminating the possibility of pregnancy and pyometra in bitches and testicular cancer in males, it inhibits (but does not prevent) breast cancer in bitches and prostate cancer in male dogs.

DOGS OLDER THAN ONE YEAR

Continue to visit the veterinarian at least once a year. There is no such disease as old age, but the bodily functions of your dog do change with age.

Together with your vet, you can develop a schedule of vaccinations and routine exams to keep your Golden healthy throughout his life.

CHECK-UPS

A dental examination is in order when the dog is between six months and one year of age so that any permanent teeth that have erupted incorrectly can be corrected. It is important to begin a brushing routine at home, using dental-care products made for dogs, such as special toothbrushes and toothpaste. Durable nylon and safe edible chews should be a part of your puppy's arsenal for good health, good teeth and pleasant breath. The vast majority of dogs three to four years old and older has diseases of the gums from lack of dental attention. Using the various types of dental chews can be very effective in controlling dental plaque.

By the time your dog is a year old, you should have become very comfortable with your local veterinarian and have agreed on scheduled visits for booster vaccinations. Blood tests should now be taken regularly, for comparative purposes, for such variables as cholesterol and triglycerides levels, thyroid hormones, liver enzymes, blood cell counts, etc.

The eyes, ears, nose and throat should be examined regularly and an annual veterinary cleaning of the teeth is a must. For teeth scaling, the dog must be anesthetized.

The eyes and ears are no longer as efficient. Liver, kidney and intestinal functions often decline. Proper dietary changes, recommended by your veterinarian, can make life more pleasant for the aging Golden Retriever and you.

SKIN PROBLEMS IN GOLDEN RETRIEVERS

Veterinarians are consulted by dog owners for skin problems more than for any other group of diseases or maladies. Dogs' skin is almost as sensitive as human skin and both suffer almost the same ailments (though the occurrence of acne in dogs is rare!). For this reason, veterinary dermatology has developed into a specialty that is practiced by many veterinarians.

Since many skin problems have visual symptoms that are almost identical, it requires the skill of an experienced veterinary dermatologist to identify and cure many of the more severe skin disorders. Pet shops sell many treatments for skin problems, but most of the treatments are directed at symptoms and not the underlying problem(s). If your dog is suffering from a skin disorder, you should seek professional assistance as quickly as possible. As with all diseases, the earlier a problem is identified and treated, the more successful is the cure.

PARASITE BITES

Many of us are allergic to mosquito bites. The bites itch, erupt and may even become infected. Dogs have the same reaction to fleas, ticks and/or mites. When you feel the prick of the mosquito as it bites you, you have a chance to kill it with your hand. Unfortunately, when your dog is bitten by a flea, tick or mite, it can only scratch it away or bite it. By the time the dog has been bitten, the parasite has done some of its damage. It may also have laid eggs to cause further problems in the near future. The itching from parasite bites is probably due to the saliva injected into the site when the parasite sucks the dog's blood.

AUTO-IMMUNE SKIN CONDITIONS

Auto-immune skin conditions are commonly referred to as being allergic to yourself, while allergies are usually inflammatory reactions to an outside stimulus. Auto-immune diseases cause

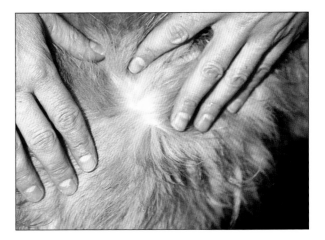

serious damage to the tissues that are involved.

The best known auto-immune disease is lupus, which affects people as well as dogs. The symptoms are variable and may affect the kidneys, bones, blood chemistry and skin. It can be fatal to both dogs and humans, though it is not thought to be transmissible. It is usually successfully treated with cortisone, prednisone or similar corticosteroid, but extensive use of these drugs can have harmful side effects.

ACRAL LICK GRANULOMA

Golden Retrievers and other dogs about the same size (like German Shepherd Dogs) have a very poorly understood syndrome called acral lick granuloma. The manifestation of the problem is the dog's tireless attack at a specific area of the body, almost always the legs. They lick so intensively that they remove the

You should inspect your Golden's skin regularly, looking for rashes and parasites. Hold the hairs apart with your hands to expose the skin.

As breathtaking as the great outdoors can be, dogs can be affected by parasites, pollen and other problems while touring the countryside.

PHOTO BY KENT AND DONNA DANNEN

Acral lick granuloma, similar to a hot spot, is of undefined origin. The dog constantly licks at a spot, usually on its leg, until the area becomes a raw, open sore.

SIMULATED MEDICAL CONDITION FOR EDUCATIONAL PURPOSES

hair and skin, leaving an ugly, large wound. There is no absolute cure, but corticosteroids are the most common treatment.

AIRBORNE ALLERGIES

Just as humans have hay fever, rose fever and other fevers from which they suffer during the pollinating season, many dogs suffer from the same allergies. When the pollen count is high, your dog might suffer but don't expect him to sneeze and have a runny nose like a human would. Dogs react to pollen allergies the same way they react to fleas—they

scratch and bite themselves. Golden Retrievers are very susceptible to airborne pollen allergies. Dogs, like humans, can be tested for allergens. Discuss the testing with your vet or a veterinary dermatologist.

FOOD PROBLEMS

FOOD ALLERGIES

Dogs are allergic to many foods that are best-sellers and highly recommended by breeders and veterinarians. Changing the brand of food that you buy may not eliminate the problem if the element to which the dog is allergic is contained in the new brand.

Recognizing a food allergy is difficult. Humans vomit or have rashes when they eat a

DENTAL HEALTH

You are your dog's caretaker and his dentist. Vets warn that plaque and tartar buildup on the teeth will damage the gums and allow bacteria to enter the dog's bloodstream, causing serious damage to the animal's vital organs. Studies show that over 50 percent of dogs have some form of gum disease before age three. Daily or weekly tooth cleaning (with a brush or soft gauze pad wipes) can add years to your dog's life.

food to which they are allergic. Dogs neither vomit nor (usually) develop a rash. They react in the same manner as they do to an airborne or flea allergy: they itch, scratch and bite, thus making the diagnosis extremely difficult. While pollen allergies and parasite bites are usually seasonal, food allergies are year-round problems.

FOOD INTOLERANCE

Food intolerance is the inability of the dog to completely digest certain foods. Puppies that may have done very well on their mother's milk may not do well on cow's milk. The result of this food intolerance may be loose bowels, passing gas and stomach pains. These are the only obvious symptoms of food intolerance and that makes diagnosis difficult.

TREATING FOOD PROBLEMS

It is possible to handle food allergies and food intolerance yourself. Put your dog on a diet that it has never had. Obviously, if it has never eaten this new food, it can't have been allergic or intolerant of it. Start with a single ingredient that is not in the dog's diet at the present time. Ingredients like chopped beef or chicken are common in dog's diets, so try something more exotic like ostrich, rabbit, fish or even just vegetables. Keep the dog on this diet (with no additives) for a month. If the symptoms of food

allergy or intolerance disappear, chances are your dog has a food allergy.

Don't think that the single ingredient cured the problem. You still must find a suitable diet and ascertain which ingredient in the old diet was objectionable. This is most easily done by adding ingredients to the new diet one at a time. Let the dog stay on the modified diet for a month before you add another ingredient. Eventually, you will determine the ingredient that caused the adverse reaction.

An alternative method is to carefully study the ingredients in the diet to which your dog is allergic or intolerant. Identify the main ingredient in this diet and eliminate the main ingredient by buying a different food that does not have that ingredient. Keep experimenting until the symptoms disappear after one month on the new diet.

HYPOTHYROIDISM

Hypothyroidism is a complex metabolic disease associated with malfunction of the thyroid gland. Symptoms include coat problems, hair loss, obesity, inactivity and lethargy, infertility and seizures. Treatment involves daily thyroid supplementation. Early-onset hypothyroidism is thought to be heritable.

A male dog flea, *Ctenocephalides canis.*

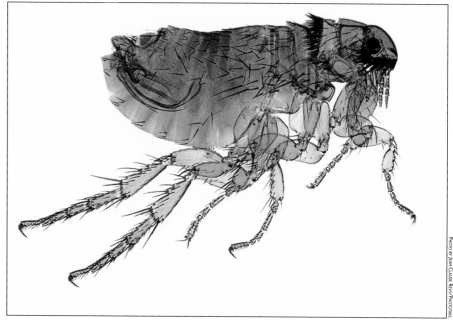

PHOTO BY JEAN CLAUDE REVY/PHOTOTAKE

EXTERNAL PARASITES

FLEAS

Of all the problems to which dogs are prone, none is more well known and frustrating than fleas. Flea infestation is relatively simple to cure but difficult to prevent. Parasites that are harbored inside the body are a bit more difficult to eradicate but they are easier to control.

To control flea infestation, you have to understand the flea's life cycle. Fleas are often thought of as a summertime problem, but centrally heated homes have changed the patterns and fleas can be found at any time of the year. The most effective method of flea control is a two-stage approach: one stage to kill the adult fleas, and the other to control the development of pre-adult fleas. Unfortunately, no single active ingredient is effective against all stages of the life cycle.

FLEA KILLER CAUTION— "POISON"

Flea-killers are poisonous. You should not spray these toxic chemicals on areas of a dog's body that he licks, including his genitals and his face. Flea killers taken internally are a better answer, but check with your vet in case internal therapy is not advised for your dog.

LIFE CYCLE STAGES

During its life, a flea will pass through four life stages: egg, larva, pupa or nymph and adult. The adult stage is the most visible and irritating stage of the flea life cycle, and this is why the majority of flea-control products concentrate on this stage. The fact is that adult fleas account for only 1% of the total flea population, and the other 99% exist in pre-adult stages, i.e., eggs, larvae and nymphs. The pre-adult stages are barely visible to the naked eye.

THE LIFE CYCLE OF THE FLEA

Eggs are laid on the dog, usually in quantities of about 20 or 30, several times a day. The adult female flea must have a blood meal before each egg-laying session. When first laid, the eggs will cling to the dog's hair, as the eggs are still moist. However, they will quickly dry out and fall from the dog, especially if the dog moves around or scratches. Many eggs will fall off in the dog's favorite area or an area in which he spends a lot of time, such as his bed.

Once the eggs fall from the dog onto the carpet or furniture, they will hatch into larvae. This takes from one to ten days. Larvae are not particularly mobile and will usually travel only a few inches from where they hatch. However, they do have a tendency to move away from bright light and heavy

> ### EN GARDE:
> ### CATCHING FLEAS OFF GUARD!
> Consider the following ways to arm yourself against fleas:
> - Add a small amount of pennyroyal or eucalyptus oil to your dog's bath. These natural remedies repel fleas.
> - Supplement your dog's food with fresh garlic (minced or grated) and a hearty amount of brewer's yeast, both of which ward off fleas.
> - Use a flea comb on your dog daily. Submerge fleas in a cup of bleach to kill them quickly.
> - Confine the dog to only a few rooms to limit the spread of fleas in the home.
> - Vacuum daily...and get all of the crevices! Dispose of the bag every few days until the problem is under control.
> - Wash your dog's bedding daily. Cover cushions where your dog sleeps with towels, and wash the towels often.

traffic—under furniture and behind doors are common places to find high quantities of flea larvae.

The flea larvae feed on dead organic matter, including adult flea feces, until they are ready to change into adult fleas. Fleas will usually remain as larvae for around seven days. After this period, the larvae will pupate into protective pupae. While inside the pupae, the larvae will undergo metamorphosis and change into

Fleas have been measured as being able to jump 300,000 times and can jump over 150 times their length in any direction, including straight up.

adult fleas. This can take as little time as a few days, but the adult fleas can remain inside the pupae waiting to hatch for up to two years. The pupae are signaled to hatch by certain stimuli, such as physical pressure—the pupae's being stepped on, heat from an animal's lying on the pupae or increased carbon-dioxide levels and vibrations—indicating that a suitable host is available.

Once hatched, the adult flea must feed within a few days. Once the adult flea finds a host, it will not leave voluntarily. It only becomes dislodged by grooming or the host animal's scratching. The adult flea will remain on the

PHOTO BY DWIGHT R. KUHN

host for the duration of its life unless forcibly removed.

TREATING THE ENVIRONMENT AND THE DOG

Treating fleas should be a two-pronged attack. First, the environment needs to be treated; this includes carpets and furniture, especially the dog's bedding and areas underneath furniture. The environment should be treated with a household spray containing an Insect Growth Regulator (IGR) and an insecticide to kill the adult fleas. Most IGRs are effective against eggs and larvae; they actually mimic the fleas' own hormones and stop the eggs and larvae from developing into adult fleas. There are currently no treatments available to attack the pupa stage of the life cycle, so the adult insecticide is used to kill the newly hatched adult fleas before they find a host. Most IGRs are active for many months, while adult insecticides are only active for a few days.

A scanning electron micrograph of a dog or cat flea, *Ctenocephalides*, magnified more than 100x. This image has been colorized for effect.

S. E. M. BY DR. DENNIS KUNKEL, UNIVERSITY OF HAWAII

THE LIFE CYCLE OF THE FLEA

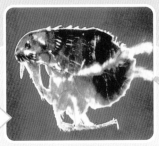

Adult

Egg

Larva

**Pupa
or
Nymph**

Fleas have been around for millions of years and have adapted to changing host animals. They are able to go through a complete life cycle in less than one month or they can extend their lives to almost two years by remaining as pupae or cocoons. They do not need blood or any other food for up to 20 months.

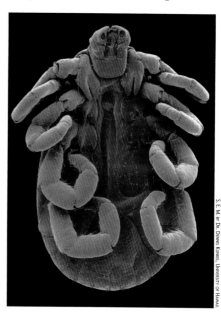

The American dog tick, *Dermacentor variabilis*, is probably the most common tick found on dogs. Look at the strength in its eight legs! No wonder it's hard to detach them.

INSECT GROWTH REGULATOR (IGR)

Two types of products should be used when treating fleas—a product to treat the pet and a product to treat the home. Adult fleas represent less than 1% of the flea population. The pre-adult fleas (eggs, larvae and pupae) represent more than 99% of the flea population and are found in the environment; it is in the case of pre-adult fleas that products containing an Insect Growth Regulator (IGR) should be used in the home.

IGRs are a new class of compounds used to prevent the development of insects. They do not kill the insect outright, but instead use the insect's biology against it to stop it from completing its growth. Products that contain methoprene are the world's first and leading IGRs. Used to control fleas and other insects, this type of IGR will stop flea larvae from developing and protect the house for up to seven months.

When treating with a household spray, it is a good idea to vacuum before applying the product. This stimulates as many pupae as possible to hatch into adult fleas. The vacuum cleaner should also be treated with an insecticide to prevent the eggs and larvae that have been collected in the vacuum bag from hatching.

The second stage of treatment is to apply an adult insecticide to the dog. Traditionally, this would be in the form of a collar or a spray, but more recent innovations include digestible insecticides that poison the fleas when they ingest the dog's blood. Alternatively, there are drops that, when placed on the back of the dog's neck, spread throughout the hair and skin to kill adult fleas.

TICKS

Though not as common as fleas, ticks are found all over the tropical and temperate world. They don't bite, like fleas; they harpoon. They dig their sharp proboscis (nose) into the dog's skin and drink the blood. Their only food and drink is dog's

S. E. M. by Dr. Dennis Kunkel, University of Hawaii

blood. Dogs can get Lyme disease, Rocky Mountain spotted fever, tick bite paralysis and many other diseases from ticks. They may live where fleas are found and they like to hide in cracks or seams in walls. They are controlled the same way fleas are controlled.

The American dog tick, *Dermacentor variabilis*, may well be the most common dog tick in many geographical areas, especially those areas where the climate is hot and humid. Most dog ticks have life expectancies of a week to six months, depending upon climatic conditions. They can neither jump nor fly, but they can crawl slowly and can range up to 16 feet to reach a sleeping or unsuspecting dog.

MITES

Just as fleas and ticks can be problematic for your dog, mites can also lead to an itchy nuisance. Microscopic in size, mites are related to ticks and generally take up permanent residence on their host animal— in this case, your dog! The term *mange* refers to any infestation caused by one of the mighty mites, of which there are six varieties that concern dog owners.

Demodex mites cause a condition known as demodicosis (sometimes called red mange or

DEER-TICK CROSSING

The great outdoors may be fun for your dog, but it also is a home to dangerous ticks. Deer ticks carry a bacterium known as *Borrelia burgdorferi* and are most active in the autumn and spring. When infections are caught early, penicillin and tetracycline are effective antibiotics, but, if left untreated, the bacteria may cause neurological, kidney and cardiac problems as well as long-term trouble with walking and painful joints.

S. E. M. BY DR. ANDREW SPIELMAN/PHOTOTAKE.

PHOTO BY DR. DENNIS KUNKEL, UNIVERSITY OF HAWAII.

The head of an American dog tick, *Dermacentor variabilis*, enlarged and colorized for effect.

The mange mite, *Psoroptes bovis*, can infest cattle and other domestic animals.

PHOTO BY JAMES HAYDEN/YOAV/PHOTOTAKE

follicular mange), in which the mites live in the dog's hair follicles and sebaceous glands in larger-than-normal numbers. This type of mange is commonly passed from the dam to her puppies and usually shows up on the puppies' muzzles, though demodicosis is not transferable from one normal dog to another. Most dogs recover from this type of mange without any treatment, though topical therapies are commonly prescribed by the vet.

The *Cheyletiellosis* mite is the hook-mouthed culprit associated

Human lice look like dog lice; the two are closely related.

PHOTO BY DWIGHT R. KUHN.

with "walking dandruff," a condition that affects dogs as well as cats and rabbits. This mite lives on the surface of the animal's skin and is readily transferable through direct or indirect contact with an affected animal. The dandruff is present in the form of scaly skin, which may or may not be itchy. If not treated, this mange can affect a whole kennel of dogs and can be spread to humans as well.

The *Sarcoptes* mite causes intense itching on the dog in the form of a condition known as scabies or sarcoptic mange. The cycle of the *Sarcoptes* mite lasts about three weeks, and the mites live in the top layer of the dog's skin (epidermis), preferably in

areas with little hair. Scabies is highly contagious and can be passed to humans. Sometimes an allergic reaction to the mite worsens the severe itching associated with sarcoptic mange.

Ear mites, *Otodectes cynotis,* lead to otodectic mange, which most commonly affects the outer ear canal of the dog, though other areas can be affected as well. Dogs with ear-mite infestation commonly scratch at their ears, causing further irritation, and shake their heads. Dark brown droppings in the outer ear confirm the diagnosis. Your vet can prescribe a treatment to flush out the ears and kill any eggs in the ears. A complete month of treatment is necessary to cure the mange.

Two other mites, less common in dogs, include *Dermanyssus gallinae* (the poultry or red mite) and *Eutrombicula alfreddugesi* (the North American mite associated with trombiculidiasis or chigger infestation). The poultry mite frequently lives on chickens, but can transfer to dogs who spend time near farm animals. Chigger infestation affects dogs in the

DO NOT MIX
Never mix parasite-control products without first consulting your vet. Some products can become toxic when combined with others and can cause fatal consequences.

NOT A DROP TO DRINK
Never allow your dog to swim in polluted water or public areas where water quality can be suspect. Even perfectly clear water can harbor parasites, many of which can cause serious to fatal illnesses in canines. Areas inhabited by waterfowl and other wildlife are especially dangerous.

Central US who have exposure to woodlands. The types of mange caused by both of these mites are treatable by vets.

INTERNAL PARASITES
Most animals—fishes, birds and mammals, including dogs and humans—have worms and other parasites that live inside their bodies. According to Dr. Herbert R. Axelrod, the fish pathologist, there are two kinds of parasites: dumb and smart. The smart parasites live in peaceful cooperation with their hosts (symbiosis), while the dumb parasites kill their hosts. Most worm infections are relatively easy to control. If they are not controlled, they weaken the host dog to the point that other medical problems occur, but they do not kill the host as dumb parasites would.

A brown dog tick, *Rhipicephalus sanguineus*, is an uncommon but annoying tick found on dogs.
PHOTO BY CAROLINA BIOLOGICAL SUPPLY/PHOTOTAKE.

PHOTO BY CAROLINA BIOLOGICAL SUPPLY/PHOTOTAKE.

The roundworm *Rhabditis* can infect both dogs and humans.

ROUNDWORMS

Average-size dogs can pass 1,360,000 roundworm eggs every day. For example, if there were only 1 million dogs in the world, the world would be saturated with thousands of tons of dog feces. These feces would contain around 15,000,000,000 roundworm eggs.

Up to 31% of home yards and children's sand boxes in the US contain roundworm eggs.

Flushing dog's feces down the toilet is not a safe practice because the usual sewage treatments do not destroy roundworm eggs.

Infected puppies start shedding roundworm eggs at three weeks of age. They can be infected by their mother's milk.

The roundworm, *Ascaris lumbricoides*.

PHOTO BY DWIGHT R. KUHN.

ROUNDWORMS

The roundworms that infect dogs are known scientifically as *Toxocara canis*. They live in the dog's intestines and shed eggs continually. It has been estimated that a dog produces about 6 or more ounces of feces every day. Each ounce of feces averages hundreds of thousands of roundworm eggs. There are no known areas in which dogs roam that do not contain roundworm eggs. The greatest danger of roundworms is that they infect people, too! It is wise to have your dog tested regularly for roundworms.

In young puppies, roundworms cause bloated bellies, diarrhea, coughing and vomiting, and are transmitted from the dam (through blood or milk). Affected puppies will not appear as animated as normal puppies. The worms appear spaghetti-like, measuring as long as 6 inches. Adult dogs can acquire roundworms through coprophagia (eating contaminated feces) or by killing rodents that carry roundworms.

Roundworm infection can kill puppies and cause severe problems in adults, as the hatched larvae travel to the lungs and trachea through the bloodstream. Cleanliness is the best preventative for roundworms. Always pick up after your dog and dispose of feces in appropriate receptacles.

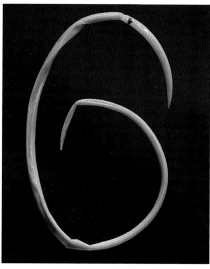

PHOTO BY DWIGHT R. KUHN.

HOOKWORMS

In the United States, dog owners have to be concerned about four different species of hookworm, the most common and most serious of which is *Ancylostoma caninum,* which prefers warm climates. The others are *Ancylostoma braziliense, Ancylostoma tubaeforme* and *Uncinaria stenocephala,* the latter of which is a concern to dogs living in the Northern US and Canada, as this species prefers cold climates. Hookworms are dangerous to humans as well as to dogs and cats, and can be the cause of severe anemia due to iron deficiency. The worm uses its teeth to attach itself to the dog's intestines and changes the site of its attachment about six times per day. Each time the worm repositions itself, the dog loses blood and can become anemic. *Ancylostoma caninum* is the most likely of the four species to cause anemia in the dog.

Symptoms of hookworm infection include dark stools, weight loss, general weakness, pale coloration and anemia, as well as possible skin problems. Fortunately, hookworms are easily purged from the affected dog with a number of medications that have proven effective. Discuss these with your vet. Most heartworm preventatives include a hookworm insecticide as well.

Owners also must be aware that hookworms can infect humans, who can acquire the larvae through exposure to contaminated feces. Since the worms cannot complete their life cycle on a human, the worms simply infest the skin and cause irritation. This condition is known as cutaneous larva migrans syndrome. As a preventative, use disposable gloves or a "poop-scoop" to pick up your dog's droppings and prevent your dog (or neighborhood cats) from defecating in children's play areas.

The hookworm, *Ancylostoma caninum*.

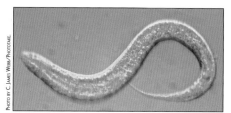

PHOTO BY C. JAMES WEBB/PHOTOTAKE.

The infective stage of the hookworm larva.

TAPEWORMS

Humans, rats, squirrels, foxes, coyotes, wolves and domestic dogs are all susceptible to tapeworm infection. Except in humans, tapeworms are usually not a fatal infection. Infected individuals can harbor 1000 parasitic worms.

Tapeworms, like some other types of worm, are hermaphroditic, meaning male and female in the same worm.

If dogs eat infected rats or mice, or anything else infected with tapeworm, they get the tapeworm disease. One month after attaching to a dog's intestine, the worm starts shedding eggs. These eggs are infective immediately. Infective eggs can live for a few months without a host animal.

The head and rostellum (the round prominence on the scolex) of a tapeworm, which infects dogs and humans.

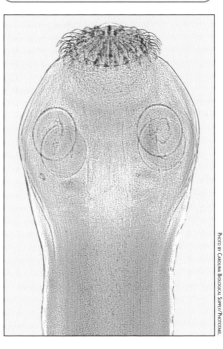

PHOTO BY CAROLINA BIOLOGICAL SUPPLY/PHOTOTAKE.

TAPEWORMS

There are many species of tapeworm, all of which are carried by fleas! The most common tapeworm affecting dogs is known as *Dipylidium caninum*. The dog eats the flea and starts the tapeworm cycle. Humans can also be infected with tapeworms—so don't eat fleas! Fleas are so small that your dog could pass them onto your hands, your plate or your food and thus make it possible for you to ingest a flea that is carrying tapeworm eggs.

While tapeworm infection is not life-threatening in dogs (smart parasite!), it can be the cause of a very serious liver disease for humans. About 50% of the humans infected with *Echinococcus multilocularis*, a type of tapeworm that causes alveolar hydatid, perish.

WHIPWORMS

In North America, whipworms are counted among the most common parasitic worms in dogs. The whipworm's scientific name is *Trichuris vulpis*. These worms attach themselves in the lower parts of the intestine, where they feed. Affected dogs may only experience upset tummies, colic and diarrhea. These worms, however, can live for months or years in the dog, beginning their larval stage in the small intestine, spending their adult stage in the large intestine and finally passing infective eggs

through the dog's feet. The only way to detect whipworms is through a fecal examination, though this is not always foolproof. Treatment for whipworms is tricky, due to the worms' unusual life-cycle pattern, and very often dogs are reinfected due to exposure to infective eggs on the ground. The whipworm eggs can survive in the environment for as long as five years; thus, cleaning up droppings in your own backyard as well as in public places is absolutely essential for sanitation purposes and the health of your dog and others.

THREADWORMS
Though less common than roundworms, hookworms and those previously mentioned, threadworms concern dog owners in the Southwestern US and Gulf Coast area where the climate is hot and humid. Living in the small intestine of the dog, this worm measures a mere 2 millimeters and is round in shape. Like that of the whipworm, the threadworm's life cycle is very complex and the eggs and larvae are passed through the feces. A deadly disease in humans, *Strongyloides* readily infects people, and the handling of feces is the most common means of transmission. Threadworms are most often seen in young puppies; bloody diarrhea and pneumonia are symptoms. Sick puppies must be isolated and treated immediately; vets recommend a follow-up treatment one month later.

HEARTWORM PREVENTATIVES

There are many heartworm preventatives on the market, many of which are sold at your veterinarian's office. These products can be given daily or monthly, depending on the manufacturer's instructions. All of these preventatives contain chemical insecticides directed at killing heartworms, which leads to some controversy among dog owners. In effect, heartworm preventatives are necessary evils, though you should determine how necessary based on your pet's lifestyle. There is no doubt that heartworm is a dreadful disease that threatens the lives of dogs. However, the likelihood of your dog's being bitten by an infected mosquito is slim in most places, and a mosquito-repellent (or an herbal remedy such as Wormwood or Black Walnut) is much safer for your dog and will not compromise his immune system (the way heartworm preventatives will). Should you decide to use the traditional preventative "medications," you can consider giving the pill every other or third month. Since the toxins in the pill will kill the heartworms at all stages of development, the pill would be effective in killing larvae, nymphs or adults, and it takes four months for the larvae to reach the adult stage. Thus, there is no rationale to poisoning the dog's system on a monthly basis. Lastly, do not give the pill during the winter months since there are no mosquitoes around to pass on their infection, unless you live in a tropical environment.

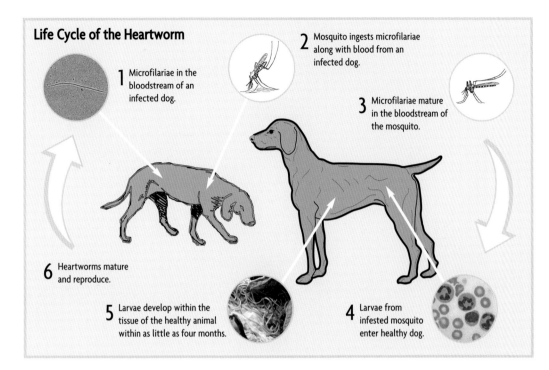

Life Cycle of the Heartworm

1 Microfilariae in the bloodstream of an infected dog.

2 Mosquito ingests microfilariae along with blood from an infected dog.

3 Microfilariae mature in the bloodstream of the mosquito.

6 Heartworms mature and reproduce.

5 Larvae develop within the tissue of the healthy animal within as little as four months.

4 Larvae from infested mosquito enter healthy dog.

HEARTWORMS

Heartworms are thin, extended worms up to 12 inches long, which live in a dog's heart and the major blood vessels surrounding it. Dogs may have up to 200 worms. Symptoms may be loss of energy, loss of appetite, coughing, the development of a pot belly and anemia.

Heartworms are transmitted by mosquitoes. The mosquito drinks the blood of an infected dog and takes in larvae with the blood. The larvae, called microfilariae, develop within the body of the mosquito and are passed on to the next dog bitten after the larvae

mature. It takes two to three weeks for the larvae to develop to the infective stage within the body of the mosquito. Dogs are usually treated at about six weeks of age and maintained on a prophylactic dose given monthly.

Blood testing for heartworms is not necessarily indicative of how seriously your dog is infected. Although this is a dangerous disease, it is not easy for a dog to be infected. Discuss the various preventatives with your vet, as there are many different types now available. Together you can decide on a safe course of prevention for your dog.

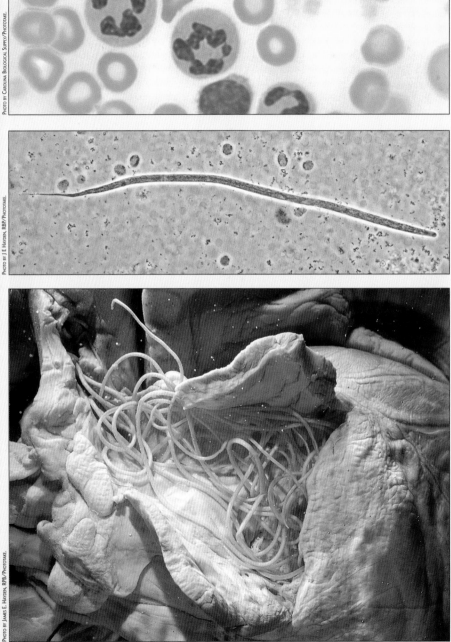

Magnified heartworm larvae, *Dirofilaria immitis.*

Heartworm, *Dirofilaria immitis.*

The heart of a dog infected with canine heartworm, *Dirofilaria immitis.*

PHOTO BY CAROLINA BIOLOGICAL SUPPLY/PHOTOTAKE.

PHOTO BY J E HAYDEN, RBP/PHOTOTAKE.

PHOTO BY JAMES E. HAYDEN, RPB/PHOTOTAKE.

HEALTH CONSIDERATIONS IN THE GOLDEN RETRIEVER

It is an unfortunate dog fact that as a breed becomes more popular, health problems increase proportionately. Sadly, Goldens are no exception. While some genetic disorders are common to most large occurs most commonly in large breeds of dogs and is known to be inherited. A severe case can render a hunting dog worthless in the field, and even a mild case can cause painful arthritis in the average house dog. Diagnosed only through X-ray examination, less severe cases

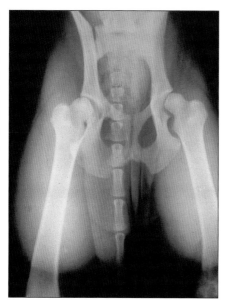 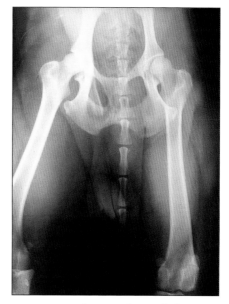

Compare the two hip joints and you'll understand dysplasia. On the left is an x-ray of a dog with hip dysplasia; on the right is an x-ray of a normal dog's pelvis.

sporting breeds, others have become more prevalent in Goldens in recent years. Hereditary disease can make life difficult or painful for the afflicted animal, and it might, in some cases, be fatal for the dog.

HIP DYSPLASIA

Simply stated, hip dysplasia (HD) means abnormal or poor development of the hip joint. It may go undetected until the dog's ability becomes impaired.

While hip dysplasia is largely an inherited condition, research shows that environmental factors play a significant role in its development. Overfeeding and feeding a diet high in calories (primarily fat) during a puppy's rapid-growth stages are suspected to be contributing factors to the

development of HD, and heavy-bodied and overweight puppies are more at risk than pups with very lean conformation.

The Orthopedic Foundation for Animals (OFA) is dedicated to establishing control programs to lower the incidence of hip dysplasia in pure-bred dogs. The X-rays of Goldens over 24 months of age are reviewed by three board-certified veterinary radiologists, whose consensus determines the scoring of the hips. OFA numbers are assigned to those scores of "Excellent," "Good" and "Fair." Hips that are designated "Borderline," "Mild," "Moderate" and "Severe" are ineligible for an OFA number.

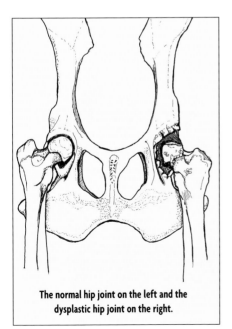

The normal hip joint on the left and the dysplastic hip joint on the right.

DO YOU KNOW ABOUT HIP DYSPLASIA?

Hip dysplasia is a fairly common condition found in Golden Retrievers, as well as other breeds. When a dog has hip dysplasia, his hind leg has an incorrectly formed hip joint. By constant use of the hip joint, it becomes more and more loose, wears abnormally and may become arthritic.

Hip dysplasia can only be confirmed with an X-ray, but certain symptoms may indicate a problem. Your Golden Retriever may have a hip dysplasia problem if he walks in a peculiar manner, hops instead of smoothly running, uses his hinds legs in unison (to keep the pressure off the weak joint), has trouble getting up from a prone position and always sits with both legs together on one side of his body.

As the dog matures, he may adapt well to life with a bad hip, but in a few years the arthritis develops and many Golden Retrievers with hip dysplasia become crippled.

Hip dysplasia is considered an inherited disease and can usually be predicted when the dog is three to nine months old, although OFA evaluation and diagnosis cannot take place until after two years old. Some experts claim that a special diet might help your puppy outgrow the bad hip, but the usual treatments are surgical: the removal of the pectineus muscle, the removal of the round part of the femur, reconstructing the pelvis and replacing the hip with an artificial one. All of these surgical interventions are expensive, but they are usually very successful. Follow the advice of your vet.

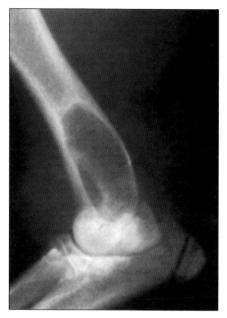

Elbow x-rays of a 4-month-old retriever's foreleg.

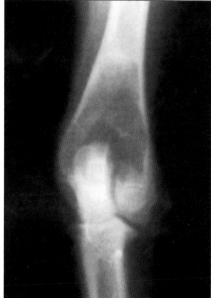

The OFA also registers carriers of elbow dysplasia, craniomandibular osteopathy (CMO), osteochondritis dessicans (OCD), ununited anchoneal process and other heritable diseases. The purpose of such screening is to eliminate affected dogs from breeding programs with the long-term goal of reducing the occurrence of hip dysplasia in affected breeds.

Goldens who show marked evidence of hip dysplasia should never be bred. Anyone looking for a healthy Golden puppy should make certain the sire and dam of any litter under consideration have their certificates of clearance.

ELBOW DYSPLASIA, OSTEOCHONDROSIS AND OCD

Similar to hip dysplasia, elbow dysplasia is a structural problem of the joints which causes front-end lameness in some large breeds of dogs. The symptoms most often appear in the growing dog, usually occurring between four and eight months of age, and range from mild to severe. Diagnosis is by x-ray examination, and affected dogs should not be used for breeding purposes.

Osteochondrosis is a degenerative cartilage disorder, which in time progresses to osteochondritis dissecans (OCD). This most often affects the front legs, and is seen primarily in large breeds.

CATARACTS

A cataract is an opacity of the lens of the eye, which has been found to be hereditary in the Golden Retriever. While some cataracts do not interfere with a dog's vision, others can progress into complete or partial blindness. Fortunately, today surgery is available to correct some types of cataracts.

Cataracts can be diagnosed by a veterinary ophthalmologic examination as early as six months of age. Eyes should be examined annually until at least three years of age as cataracts can occur later in the dog's life. All Goldens should be cleared before breeding, and affected animals should not be bred.

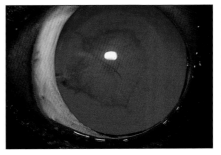

Left: The typical posterior subcapsular cataract appears between one and two years of age, but rarely progresses to where the animal has visual problems.

RETINAL DEFECTS

Progressive retinal atrophy (PRA) and retinal dysplasia (RD) are the two most common inherited retinal defects of the retina (or light receptor area of the eye). The Canine Eye Registration Foundation (CERF) works in conjunction with board-certified canine ophthalmologists to help eliminate heritable eye defects

Your Golden Retriever's eyes should be clear and bright. Any cloudiness or opacity on the lens could indicate a potential problem.

from pure-bred dogs. Only members or Diplomats of the American College of Veterinary Ophthalmologists (ACVO) are allowed to collect data. To be certified, dogs must be permanently identified (via tattoo, microchip or DNA profile) and pass a painless examination for heritable eye diseases. Unlike the progressive deterioration of PRA, RD does not result in total blindness, but will affect a working dog's ability to function at a chosen task.

The outcome of a dog's CERF examination will be stored in the database, created to help generate research reports about the incidence of the diseases in each breed. The dog's names are never revealed in these reports. Your vet or CERF can connect you with a board-certified ophthalmologist to acquire your dog's eye clearance.

EPILEPSY

Epilepsy is a seizure disorder caused by abnormal electrical patterns in the brain. It affects almost all breeds and mixed breeds, although a higher incidence is found in Golden Retrievers.

Primary epilepsy, also known as idiopathic, genetic, inherited or true epilepsy, is difficult to diagnose and there is no specific test for the disease. Primary epilepsy usually occurs between

PET ADVANTAGES

If you do not intend to show or breed your new puppy, your veterinarian will probably recommend that you spay your female or neuter your male. Some people believe neutering leads to weight gain, but if you feed and exercise your dog properly, this is easily avoided. Spaying or neutering can actually have many positive outcomes, such as:

• training becomes easier, as the dog focuses less on the urge to mate and more on you!

• females are protected from unplanned pregnancy as well as ovarian and uterine cancers.

• males are guarded from testicular tumors and have a reduced risk of developing prostate cancer.

Talk to your vet regarding the right age to spay/neuter and other aspects of the procedure.

the ages of six months and five years of age.

Secondary epilepsy refers to seizures caused by viral or infectious disease, metabolic disorders, chemical or nutritional imbalance or traumatic injury. Seizures are also associated with hypothyroidism, which is an inherited auto-immune disease common to many pure-bred dogs.

Although epilepsy is difficult to diagnose, dogs suffering recurring seizures, especially from an early age, are unsuitable breeding candidates.

MEDICAL PROBLEMS SEEN IN
GOLDEN RETRIEVERS

Condition	Age Affected	Cause	Area Affected
Acral Lick Granuloma	Any age	Unknown	Legs
Cataracts	6 mos. to 3 years	Congenital	Eye
Cleft Palate/Harelip	Newborns	Congenital	Hard or soft palate
Elbow Dysplasia	4 to 7 mos.	Congenital	Elbow joint
Epilepsy	6 mos. to 5 years	Congenital or other	Brain
Gastric Dilatation (Bloat)	Older dogs	Swallowing air	Stomach
Hip Dysplasia	4 to 9 mos.	Congenital	Hip joint
Patellar Luxation	Any age	Congenital or acquired	Kneecaps
Progressive Retinal Atrophy	Older dogs	Congenital	Eye
Retinal Dysplasia	Older dogs	Congenital	Eye
Urolithiasis	Adult	Cystine uroliths/stones	Kidney/Bladder
Von Willebrand's Disease	Birth	Congenital	Blood

The term *old* is a qualitative term. For dogs, as well as their masters, old is relative. Certainly we can all distinguish between a puppy Golden Retriever and an adult Golden Retriever—there are the obvious physical traits, such as size, appearance and facial expressions, and personality traits. Puppies that are nasty are very rare. Puppies and young dogs like to play with children. Children's natural exuberance is a good match for the seemingly endless energy of young dogs. They like to run, jump, chase and retrieve. When dogs grow up and cease their interaction with children, they are often thought of as being too old to play with the kids.

On the other hand, if a Golden Retriever is only exposed to people over 60 years of age, its life will normally be less active and it will not seem to be getting old as its activity level slows down.

If people live to be 100 years old, dogs live to be 20 years old. While this is a good rule of thumb, it is very inaccurate. When trying to compare dog years to human years, you cannot make a generalization about all dogs. You can make the generalization that 11 or 12 years is a good lifespan for a Golden Retriever, which is quite good compared to

THE GOLDEN YEARS

The bottom line is simply that a dog is getting old when *you* think it is getting old because it slows down in its general activities, including walking, running, eating, jumping and retrieving. On the other hand, certain activities increase, like more sleeping, more barking and more repetition of habits like going to the door without being called when you put your coat on.

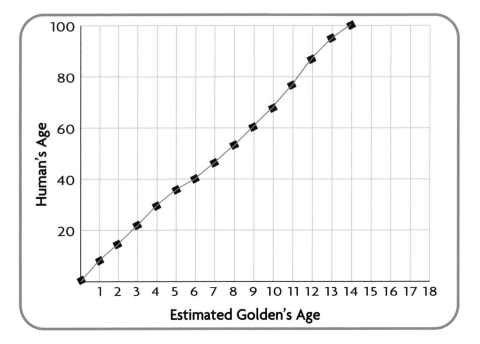

some other pure-bred dogs that may only live to 8 or 9 years of age. Some Golden Retrievers have been known to live to 15 years. Dogs are generally considered mature within three years, but they can reproduce even earlier. So the first three years of a dog's life are like seven times that of comparable humans. That means a 3-year-old dog is like a 21-year-old human. As the curve of comparison shows, there is no hard and fast rule for comparing dog and human ages. The comparison is made even more difficult, for not all humans age at the same rate...and human females live longer than human males.

SIGNS OF AGING

An old dog starts to show one or more of the following symptoms:

- Sleep patterns are deeper and longer and the old dog is harder to awaken.

- Food intake diminishes.

- Responses to calls, whistles and other signals are ignored more and more.

- Eye contacts do not evoke tail wagging (assuming they once did).

- The hair on its face and paws starts to turn gray. The color breakdown usually starts around the eyes and mouth.

WHAT TO LOOK FOR IN SENIORS

Most veterinarians and behaviorists use the seven-year mark as the time to consider a dog a "senior." The term "senior" does not imply that the dog is geriatric and has begun to fail in mind and body. Aging is essentially a slowing process. Humans readily admit that they feel a difference in their activity level from age 20 to 30, and then from 30 to 40, etc. By treating the seven-year-old dog as a senior, owners are able to implement certain therapeutic and preventative medical strategies with the help of their veterinarians. A senior-care program should include at least two veterinary visits per year, screening sessions to determine the dog's health status, as well as nutritional counseling. Veterinarians determine the senior dog's health status through a blood smear for a complete blood count, serum chemistry profile with electrolytes, urinalysis, blood pressure check, electrocardiogram, ocular tonometry (pressure on the eyeball) and dental prophylaxis.

Such an extensive program for senior dogs is well advised before owners start to see the obvious physical signs of aging, such as slower and inhibited movement, graying, increased sleep/nap periods and disinterest in play and other activity. This preventative program promises a longer, healthier life for the aging dog. Among the physical problems common in aging dogs are the loss of sight and hearing, arthritis, kidney and liver failure, diabetes mellitus, heart disease and Cushing's disease (a hormonal disease).

In addition to the physical manifestations discussed, there are some behavioral changes and problems related to aging dogs. Dogs suffering from hearing or

NOTICING THE SIGNS

The symptoms listed below are symptoms that gradually appear and become more noticeable. They are not life-threatening; however, the symptoms below are to be taken very seriously and a discussion with your veterinarian is warranted:

• Your dog cries and whimpers when it moves and stops running completely.

• Convulsions start or become more serious and frequent. The usual convulsion (spasm) is when the dog stiffens and starts to tremble, being unable or unwilling to move. The seizure usually lasts for 5 to 30 minutes.

• Your dog drinks more water and urinates more frequently. Wetting and bowel accidents take place indoors without warning.

• Vomiting becomes more and more frequent.

WHAT THE OWNER CAN LOOK FOR

IF YOU NOTICE...

IT COULD INDICATE...

IF YOU NOTICE...	IT COULD INDICATE...
Discoloration of teeth and gums, foul breath, loss of appetite	Abcesses, gum disease, mouth lesions
Lumps, bumps, cysts, warts, fatty tumors	Cancers
Cloudiness of eyes, apparent loss of sight	Cataracts, lenticular sclerosis, progressive retinal atrophy, retinal dysplasia, blindness
Flaky coat, alopecia (hair loss)	Hormonal problems, hypothyroidism
Obesity, appetite loss, excessive weight gain	Various problems
Household accidents, increased urination	Diabetes, kidney or bladder disease
Increased thirst	Kidney disease, diabetes mellitus
Change in sleeping habits, coughing	Heart disease
Difficulty moving	Arthritis, degenerative joint disease, spondylosis (degenerative spine disease)

IF THE OWNER NOTICES ANY OF THESE SIGNS, AN APPOINTMENT SHOULD BE MADE IMMEDIATELY WITH THE VETERINARIAN FOR A THOROUGH EVALUATION.

vision loss, dental discomfort or arthritis can become aggressive. Likewise. the near-deaf and/or blind dog may be startled more easily and react in an unexpectedly aggressive manner. Seniors suffering from senility can become more impatient and irritable. Housesoiling accidents are associated with loss of mobility, kidney problems, loss of sphincter control as well as plaque accumulation, physiological brain changes and reactions to medications. Older dogs, just like young puppies, suffer from separation anxiety, which can lead to excessive barking, whining, housesoiling and destructive behavior. Seniors may become fearful of everyday sounds, such as vacuum cleaners, heaters, thunder and passing traffic. Some dogs have difficulty

sleeping, due to discomfort, the need for frequent potty visits and the like.

Owners should avoid spoiling the older dog with too many fatty treats. Obesity is a common problem in older dogs and subtracts years from their lives. Keep the senior dog as trim as possible since excessive weight puts additional stress on the body's vital organs. Some breeders recommend supplementing the diet with foods high in fiber and lower in calories. Adding fresh vegetables and marrow broth to the senior's diet makes a tasty, low-calorie, low-fat supplement. Vets also offer specialty diets for senior dogs that are worth exploring.

Your dog, as he nears his twilight years, needs his owner's patience and good care more than ever. Never punish an older dog for an accident or abnormal behavior. For all the years of love, protection and companionship that your dog has provided, he deserves special attention and

SENIOR DIETS

Your senior dog may lose interest in eating, not because he's less hungry but because his senses of smell and taste have diminished. The old chow simply does not smell as good as it once did. Additionally, older dogs use less energy and thereby can sustain themselves on less food.

courtesies. The older dog may need to relieve himself at 3 a.m. because he can no longer hold it for eight hours. Older dogs may not be able to remain crated for more than two or three hours. It may be time to give up a sofa or chair to your old friend. Although he may not seem as enthusiastic about your attention and petting, he does appreciate the considerations you offer as he gets older.

Your Golden Retriever does not understand why his world is slowing down. Owners must make the transition into the golden years as pleasant and rewarding as possible.

WHAT TO DO WHEN THE TIME COMES
You are never fully prepared to make a rational decision about putting your dog to sleep. It is very obvious that you love your Golden Retriever or you would not be reading this book. Putting a loved dog to sleep is extremely difficult. It is a decision that must be made with your veterinarian. You are usually forced to make the decision when one of the life-threatening symptoms listed above becomes serious enough for you to seek medical (veterinary) help.

If the prognosis of the malady indicates the end is near and your beloved pet will only suffer more and experience no enjoyment for the balance of its life, then euthanasia is the right choice.

TALK ABOUT IT
The more open discussion you have about the whole stressful occurrence of losing your dog, the easier it will be for you when the time comes.

WHAT IS EUTHANASIA?

Euthanasia derives from the Greek, meaning "good death." In other words, it means the planned, painless killing of a dog suffering from a painful, incurable condition, or who is so aged that he cannot walk, see, eat or control his excretory functions.

Euthanasia is usually accomplished by injection with an overdose of an anesthesia or barbiturate. Aside from the prick of the needle, the experience is usually painless.

COPING WITH LOSS

The decision to euthanize your dog is never easy. The days during which the dog becomes ill and the end occurs can be unusually stressful for you. If this is your first experience with the death of a loved one, you may need the comfort dictated by your religious beliefs. If you are the head of the family and have children, you should have involved them in the decision of putting your Golden Retriever to sleep. Usually your dog can be maintained on drugs for a few days while it is kept in the clinic in order to give you ample time to

make a decision. During this time, talking with members of the family or religious representatives, or even people who have lived through this same experience, can ease the burden of your inevitable decision. In any case, euthanasia is painful and stressful for the family of the dog. Unfortunately, it does not end there.

THE FINAL RESTING PLACE

Dogs can have the same privileges as humans. They can be buried in a pet cemetery in a burial container (very expensive); buried in your yard in a place suitably marked with a stone, newly planted tree or bush; or cremated with the ashes being given to you.

All of these options should be discussed frankly and openly with your veterinarian. Do not be afraid to ask financial questions. Cremations are usually mass burnings and the ashes you get may not be only the ashes of your beloved dog. If you want a private cremation, there are small crematoriums available to all veterinary clinics. Your vet can usually arrange for this, but it may be a little more expensive.

GETTING ANOTHER DOG?

The grief of losing your beloved dog will be as lasting as the grief of losing a human friend or relative. In most cases, if your dog died of old age (if there is

Discuss the option of a pet cemetery with your vet.

such a thing), he had slowed down considerably. Do you want a new Golden Retriever puppy to replace him? Or are you better off in finding a more mature Golden Retriever, say two to three years of age, which will usually be housetrained and will have an already developed personality. In this case, you can find out if you like each other after a few hours of being together.

The decision is, of course, your own. Do you want another Golden Retriever? Perhaps you want a smaller or larger dog? How much do you want to spend on a dog? Look in your local newspapers for advertisements of breeders in your area, or, better yet, consult your local society for the prevention of cruelty to animals to adopt a dog. It is harder to find puppies at an animal shelter, but there are often many adult dogs in

Cemeteries for pets sometimes have special areas for the ashes of your beloved pet.

need of new homes. You may be able to find another Golden Retriever, or you may choose another breed or a mixed-breed dog. Private breeders are the best source for high-quality pure-bred puppies and dogs.

Whatever you decide, do it as quickly as possible. Most people usually buy the same breed because they know (and love) the characteristics of that breed. Then, too, they often know people who have the same breed and perhaps they are lucky enough that one of their friends expects a litter soon. What could be better?

CDS: COGNITIVE DYSFUNCTION SYNDROME
"Old Dog Syndrome"

There are many ways to evaluate "old-dog syndrome." Veterinarians have defined CDS (cognitive dysfunction syndrome) as the gradual deterioration of cognitive abilities. These are indicated by changes in the dog's behavior. When a dog changes his routine response, and maladies have been eliminated as the cause of these behavioral changes, then CDS is the usual diagnosis.

More than half the dogs over eight years old suffer from some form of CDS. The older the dog, the more chance he has of suffering from CDS. In humans, doctors often dismiss the CDS behavioral changes as part of "winding down."

There are four major signs of CDS: frequent accidents inside the home, sleeps much more or much less than normal, acts confused and fails to respond to social stimuli.

SYMPTOMS OF CDS

FREQUENT HOUSEBREAKING ACCIDENTS
- *Urinates in the house.*
- *Defecates in the house.*
- *Doesn't signal that he wants to go out.*

SLEEP PATTERNS
- *Awakens more slowly.*
- *Sleeps more than normal during the day.*
- *Sleeps less during the night.*

CONFUSION
- *Goes outside and just stands there.*
- *Appears confused with a faraway look in his eyes.*
- *Hides more often.*
- *Doesn't recognize friends.*
- *Doesn't come when called.*
- *Walks around listlessly and without a destination.*

FAILURE TO RESPOND TO SOCIAL STIMULI
- *Comes to people less frequently, whether called or not.*
- *Doesn't tolerate petting for more than a short time.*
- *Doesn't come to the door when you return home from work.*

Since we can never expect a dog to speak our language, we must learn to speak "dog." A puppy showing you his belly indicates his total submission and trust.

As a Golden Retriever owner, you have selected your dog so that you and your loved ones can have a companion, a protector, a friend and a four-legged family member. You invest time, money and effort to care for and train the family's new charge. Of course, this chosen canine behaves perfectly! Well, perfectly like a *dog*.

THINK LIKE A DOG
Dogs do not think like humans, nor do humans think like dogs, though we try. Unfortunately, a dog is incapable of figuring out how humans think, so the responsibility falls on the owner to adopt a proper canine mindset. Dogs cannot rationalize, and dogs exist in the present moment. Many dog

MORE HARM THAN GOOD
Punishment is rarely necessary for a misbehaving dog. Dogs that habitually misbehave probably had a poor education and they do not know what is expected of them. They need training. Disciplinary behavior on your part usually does more harm than good.

owners make the mistake in training of thinking that they can reprimand their dogs for something he did a while ago. Basically, you cannot even reprimand a dog for something he did 20 seconds ago! Either catch him in the act or forget it! It is a waste of your and your dog's time—in his mind, you are reprimanding him for whatever he is doing at that moment.

The following behavioral problems represent some which owners most commonly encounter. Every dog is unique and every situation is unique. No author could purport to solve your Golden Retriever's problem simply by reading a script. Here we outline some basic "dogspeak" so that owners' chances of solving behavioral problems are increased. Discuss bad habits with your

IT'S PLAY TIME

Physical games like pulling contests, wrestling, jumping and teasing should not be encouraged. Inciting the dog's crazy behavior tends to confuse a dog. The owner has to be able to control his dog at all times; even in play, your dog has to know that you're the leader and that you decide when to play and when to behave mannerly.

veterinarian and he/she can recommend a behavioral specialist to consult in appropriate cases. Since behavioral abnormalities are the leading reason that owners abandon their pets, we hope that you will make a valiant effort to solve your Golden Retriever's problem. Patience and understanding are virtues that dwell in every pet-loving household.

AGGRESSION

Although nobody considers the Golden Retriever to be a mean or vicious breed, aggression is always a concern among dog owners. Goldens are not naturally aggressive, but aggressive tendencies can show up in dogs of any breed for a number of reasons.

Aggression, when not controlled, always becomes dangerous. An aggressive dog, no matter the size, may lunge at, bite or even attack a person or another dog. Aggressive behavior is not to be tolerated. It is more than just inappropriate behavior; it is not safe. It is painful for a family to watch their dog become unpredictable in his behavior to the point where they are afraid of him. While not all aggressive behavior is dangerous, growling, baring teeth, etc., can be frightening. It is important to ascertain why the dog is acting in this manner. Aggression is a display of dominance, and the dog should not have the dominant role in its pack, which is, in this case, your family.

It is important not to challenge an aggressive dog, as this could provoke an attack. Observe your Golden Retriever's

Golden Retriever puppies learn manners from their dams. Licking the neck of the dam indicates the subordination of the pup to the pack leader.

body language. Does he make direct eye contact and stare? Does he try to make himself as large as possible: head up, chest out, tail erect? Height and size signify authority in a dog pack—being taller or "above" another dog literally means that he is "above" in the social status. These body signals tell you that your Golden Retriever thinks he is in charge, a problem that needs to be addressed. An aggressive dog is unpredictable: you never know when he is going to strike and what he is going to do. You cannot understand why a dog that is playful and loving one minute is growling and snapping the next.

The best solution is to consult a behavioral specialist, one who has experience with the Golden Retriever if possible. Together, perhaps you can pinpoint the cause of your dog's aggression and do something about it. An aggressive dog cannot be trusted, and a dog that cannot be trusted is not safe to have as a family pet. If the pet Golden Retriever becomes untrustworthy, he cannot be kept in the home with the family. The family must get rid of the dog. In the very worst case, the dog must be euthanized.

AGGRESSION TOWARD OTHER DOGS
In general, a dog's aggressive behavior toward another dog

INCOMPLETE SOCIALIZATION

Fear in a grown dog is often the result of improper or incomplete socialization as a pup, or it can be the result of a traumatic experience he suffered when young. Keep in mind that the term "traumatic" is relative—something that you would not think twice about can leave a lasting negative impression on a puppy. If the dog experiences a similar situation later in life, he may try to fight back to protect himself. Again, this behavior is very unpredictable, especially if you do not know what is triggering his fear.

EYE CONTACT

If you and your on-lead dog are approached by a larger, running dog that is not restrained, walk away from the dog as quickly as possible. Don't allow your dog to make eye contact with the other dog. You should not make eye contact either. In dog terms, eye contact indicates a challenge.

DOMINANT AGGRESSION

A social hierarchy is firmly established in a wild dog pack. The dog wants to dominate those under him and please those above him. Dogs know that there must be a leader. If you are not the obvious choice for emperor, the dog will assume the throne! These conflicting innate desires are what a dog owner is up against when he sets about training a dog. In training a dog to obey commands, the owner is reinforcing that he is the top dog in the "pack" and that the dog should, and should want to, serve his superior. Thus, the owner is suppressing the dog's urge to dominate by modifying

stems from not enough exposure to other dogs at an early age. If other dogs make your Golden Retriever nervous and agitated, he will lash out as a defensive mechanism. A dog who has not received sufficient exposure to other canines tends to believe that he is the only dog on the planet. The animal becomes so dominant that he does not even show signs that he is fearful or threatened. Without growling or any other physical signal as a warning, he will lunge at and bite the other dog. A way to correct this is to let your Golden Retriever approach another dog when walking on lead. Watch very closely and at the very first sign of aggression, correct your Golden Retriever and pull him away. Scold him for any sign of discomfort, and then praise him when he ignores or tolerates the other dog. Keep this up until he stops the aggressive behavior, learns to ignore the other dog or accepts other dogs. Praise him lavishly for his correct behavior.

Meeting along the trail is enjoyable for the hikers. When introducing your Golden to strange dogs, it's best to keep all dogs on lead in case one dog becomes aggressive.

his behavior and making him obedient.

An important part of training is taking every opportunity to reinforce that you are the leader. The simple action of making your Golden Retriever sit to wait for his food says that you control when he eats and that he is dependent on you for food. Although it may be difficult, do not give in to your dog's wishes every time he whines at you or looks at you with his pleading eyes. It is a constant effort to show the dog that his place in the pack is at the bottom. This is not meant to sound cruel or ruthless. You love your Golden Retriever and you should treat him with care

DOGGIE DEMOCRACY

Your dog inherited the pack-leader mentality. He only knows about pecking order. He instinctively wants to be top dog, but you have to convince him that you are boss. There is no such thing as living in a democracy with your dog. You are the leader; you make the rules.

and affection. You (hopefully) did not get a dog just so you could control another creature. Dog training is not about being cruel or feeling important, it is about molding the dog's behavior into what is acceptable and teaching him to live by your rules. In theory, it is quite

Not usually considered "pack dogs," Golden Retrievers generally do very well in large groups. Some owners own a half dozen dogs and allow them to romp and play together constantly.

simple: catch him in appropriate behavior and reward him for it. Add a dog into the equation and it becomes a bit more trying, but as a rule of thumb, positive reinforcement is what works best.

With a dominant dog, punishment and negative reinforcement can have the opposite effect of what you are after. It can make a dog fearful and/or act out aggressively if he feels he is being challenged. Remember, a dominant dog perceives himself at the top of the social heap and will fight to defend his perceived status. The best way to prevent that is never to give him reason to think that he is in control in the first place. If you are having trouble training your Golden Retriever and it seems as if he is constantly challenging your authority, seek the help of an obedience trainer or behavioral specialist. A professional will work with both you and your dog to teach you effective techniques to use at home. Beware of trainers who rely on excessively harsh methods; scolding is necessary now and then, but the focus in your training should always be on positive reinforcement.

If you can isolate what brings out the fear reaction, you can help the dog get over it. Supervise your Golden Retriever's interactions with people and other dogs, and praise the dog when it goes well. If he starts to act aggressively in a situation, correct him and remove him from the situation. Do not let people approach the dog and start petting him without your express permission. That way, you can have the dog sit to accept petting, and praise him when he behaves properly. You are focusing on praise and on

BELLY UP!

When two dogs are introduced, they will naturally establish who is dominant. This may involve one dog placing his front paws on the other's shoulders, or one dog rolling over and exposing his belly, thereby assuming a submissive status. If neither dog submits, they may fight until one has been pinned down. This behaviour can be upsetting for owners to watch, especially if your dog takes one look and throws himself on the ground. The biggest mistake you can make is to interfere, pulling on the leads and confusing the dogs. If you don't allow them to establish their pecking order, you undermine the pack mentality, which can cause your dog great stress. If you separate dogs in the middle of a fight, the interference may incite them to attack each other viciously. Your best choice is to stay out of it!

modifying his behavior by rewarding him when he acts appropriately. By being gentle and by supervising his interactions, you are showing him that there is no need to be afraid or defensive.

NO KISSES

We all love our dogs and our dogs love us. They show their love and affection by licking us. This is not a very sanitary practice as dogs lick and sniff in some unsavory places. Kissing your dog on the mouth is strictly forbidden, as parasites can be transmitted in this manner.

SEXUAL BEHAVIOR

Dogs exhibit certain sexual behaviors that may have influenced your choice of male or female when you first bought your Golden Retriever. Spaying/neutering will eliminate these behaviors, but if you are purchasing a dog that you wish to breed, you should be aware of what you will have to deal with throughout the dog's life.

Female dogs usually have two estruses per year with each season lasting about three weeks. These are the only times in which a female dog will mate, and she usually will not allow this until the second week of the cycle. If a bitch is not bred during the heat cycle, it is not uncommon for her to experience a false pregnancy, in which her mammary glands swell and she exhibits maternal tendencies toward toys or other objects.

Mounting, most often seen in unneutered males, is not merely a sexual expression but also one of dominance. Be consistent and persistent and you will find that you can "move mounters."

CHEWING

The national canine pastime is chewing! Every dog loves to sink his "canines" into a tasty bone, but sometimes that bone is attached to his owner's hand!

Dogs need to chew, to massage their gums, to make their new teeth feel better and to exercise their jaws. This is a natural behavior deeply imbedded in all things canine. Our role as owners is not to stop chewing, but to redirect it to positive, chew-worthy objects. Be an informed owner and purchase proper chew toys like strong nylon bones made for active dogs like your Golden Retriever. Be sure that the devices are safe and durable, since your dog's safety is at risk.

Again, the owner is responsible for ensuring a dog-proof environment. The best answer is prevention; that is, put your shoes, handbags and other tasty objects in their proper places (out of the reach of the growing canine mouth). Direct puppies to their toys whenever you see them tasting the furniture legs or your sleeve. Make a loud noise to attract the pup's attention and immediately escort him to his chew toy and engage him with the toy for at least four minutes, praising and encouraging him all the while.

Some trainers recommend deterrents, such as hot pepper or another bitter spice or a product designed for this purpose, to discourage the dog from chewing unwanted objects. This is sometimes reliable, though not as often as the

SMILE!
Dogs and humans may be the only animals that smile. Dogs imitate the smile on their owner's face when he greets a friend. The dog only smiles at his human friends. He never smiles at another dog or cat. Usually he rolls up his lips and shows his teeth in a clenched mouth while he rolls over onto his back, begging for a soft scratch.

manufacturers of such products claim. Test out the product with your own dog before investing in a case of it.

DIGGING
Digging, which is seen as a destructive behavior to humans, is actually quite a natural behavior in dogs. Although your Golden Retriever is not one of the "earth dogs" (also known as terriers), his desire to dig can be irrepressible and most frustrating to his owners. When digging occurs in your yard, it is actually a normal behavior

redirected into something the dog can do in his everyday life. In the wild, a dog would be actively seeking food, making his own shelter, etc. He would be using his paws in a purposeful manner for his survival. Since you provide him with food and shelter, he has no need to use his paws for these purposes, and so the energy that he would be using manifests itself in the form of little holes all over your yard and flower beds.

MOVING MOUNTERS

Males, whether castrated or not, will mount almost anything: a pillow, your leg or, much to your horror, even your neighbour's leg. As with other types of inappropriate behavior, the dog must be corrected while in the act, which for once is not difficult. Often he will not let go! While a puppy is experimenting with his very first urges, his owners feel he needs to "sow his oats" and allow the pup to mount. As the pup grows into a full-size dog, with full-size urges, it becomes a nuisance and an embarrassment. Males always appear as if they are trying to "save the race," more determined and stronger than imaginable. While altering the dog at an appropriate age will limit the dog's desire, it usually does not remove it entirely.

Perhaps your dog is digging as a reaction to boredom—it is somewhat similar to someone eating a whole bag of chips in front of the TV—because they are there and there is not anything better to do! Basically, the answer is to provide the dog with adequate play and exercise so that his mind and paws are occupied, and so that he feels as if he is doing something useful.

Of course, digging is easiest to control if it is stopped as soon as possible, but it is often hard to catch a dog in the act, especially if he is alone in the yard during the day. If your dog is a compulsive digger and is not easily distracted by other activities, you can designate an area on your property where it is okay for him to dig. If you catch him digging in an off-limits area of the yard, immediately bring him to the approved area and praise him for digging there. Keep a close eye on him so that you can catch him in the act—that is the only way to make him understand what is permitted and what is not. If you bring him to a hole he dug an hour ago and tell him "No," he will understand that you are not fond of holes, or dirt, or flowers. If you catch him while he is stifle-deep in your tulips, that is when he will get your message.

NO JUMPING

Stop a dog from jumping before he jumps. If he is getting ready to jump onto you, simply walk away. If he jumps on you before you can turn away, lift your knee so that it bumps him in the chest. Do not be forceful. Your dog will realize that jumping up is not a productive way of getting attention.

JUMPING UP

Jumping up is a dog's friendly way of saying hello! Some dog owners do not mind when their dog jumps up, which is fine for them. The problem arises when guests come to the house and the dog greets them in the same manner—whether they like it or not! However friendly the greeting may be, chances are your visitors will not appreciate being knocked over by your boisterous Golden Retriever. The dog will not be able to distinguish upon whom he can jump and whom he cannot. Therefore, it is probably best to discourage this behavior entirely.

Pick a command such as "Off" (avoid using "Down" since you will use that for the dog to lie down) and tell him "Off" when he jumps up. Place him on the ground on all fours and have him sit, praising him the whole time. Always lavish him with praise and petting when he is in the sit position. That way you are still giving him a warm affectionate greeting, because you are as excited to see him as he is to see you!

BARKING

Dogs cannot talk—oh, what they would say if they could! Instead, barking is a dog's way of "talking." It can be somewhat frustrating because it is not always easy to tell what a dog means by his bark—is he excited, happy, frightened or angry? Whatever it is that the dog is trying to say, he should not be punished for barking. Only when the barking becomes excessive, and when the excessive barking becomes a bad habit, does the behavior need to be modified.

Jumping up is unacceptable behavior in any dog, especially one as heavy as the Golden Retriever. Although he thinks he's being friendly, jumping up can be dangerous and must be properly handled.

If an intruder came into your home in the middle of the night and your Golden Retriever barked a warning, wouldn't you be pleased? You would probably deem your dog a hero, a wonderful guardian and protector of the home. However, if a friend drops by unexpectedly and rings the doorbell and is greeted with a sudden sharp bark, you would probably be annoyed at the dog. But in reality, isn't this just the same behavior? The dog does not know any better...unless he sees who is at the door and it is someone he knows, he will bark as a means of vocalizing that his

There are no limits to the talents of the Golden Retriever. While not many Goldens are employed as sled dogs, this gifted Golden joins his Samoyed housemates to be the exception!

THE DOG IN CHARGE
Barking is your dog's way of protecting you. If he barks at a stranger walking past your house, a moving car or a fleeing cat, he is merely exercising his responsibility to protect his pack (YOU) and territory from a perceived intruder. Since the "intruder" usually keeps going, the dog thinks his barking chased it away and he feels fulfilled. This behavior leads your overly vocal friend to believe that he is the "dog in charge."

(and your) territory is being threatened. While your friend is not posing a threat, it is all the same to the dog. Barking is his means of letting you know that

there is an intrusion, whether friend or foe, on your property. This type of barking is instinctive and should not be discouraged.

Excessive habitual barking, however, is a problem that should be corrected early on. As your Golden Retriever grows up, you will be able to tell when his barking is purposeful and when it is for no reason. You will become able to distinguish your dog's different barks and their meanings. For example, the bark when someone comes to the door will be different from the bark when he is excited to see you. It is similar to a person's tone of voice, except that the dog has to rely totally on tone of voice because he does not have the benefit of using words. An incessant barker will be evident at an early age.

There are some things that encourage a dog to bark. For example, if your dog barks non-stop for a few minutes and you give him a treat to quiet him, he believes that you are rewarding him for barking. He will associate barking with getting a treat, and will do it until he is rewarded.

FOOD STEALING
Is your dog devising ways of stealing food from your kitchen cabinets or pantry? If so, you must answer the following questions: Is your Golden Retriever hungry, or is he "constantly famished" like every other chow hound? Why is there food on the counter top within the dog's reach? Face it, some dogs are more food-motivated than others. Some dogs are totally obsessed by a filet of beef and can only think of their next meal. Food stealing is terrific fun and always yields a great reward—*food*, glorious food.

The owner's goal, therefore, is to make the "reward" less rewarding, even startling! Plant a shaker can (an empty can with coins inside) on the counter so that it catches your pooch offguard. There are other devices available that will surprise the dog when he is looking for a mid-afternoon snack. Such remote-control

---

THE "QUIET" COMMAND

To encourage proper barking, you can teach your dog the command "Quiet." When someone comes to the door and the dog barks a few times, praise him. Talk to him soothingly and when he stops barking, tell him "Quiet" and continue to praise him. In this sense you are letting him bark his warning, which is an instinctive behavior, and then rewarding him for being quiet after a few barks. You may initially reward him with a treat after he has been quiet for a few minutes.

devices, though not the first choice of some trainers, allow the correction to come from the object instead of the owner. These devices are also useful to keep the snacking hound from napping on furniture that is forbidden.

BEGGING

Just like food stealing, begging is a favorite pastime of hungry puppies! It yields that same great reward—*food!* Dogs quickly learn that their owners keep the "good food" for themselves, and that we humans do not dine on   kibble alone. Begging is a conditioned response related to a specific stimulus, time and place. The sounds of the kitchen, cans and bottles opening, crinkling bags, the smell of food in preparation, etc., will excite the chow hound, and soon the paws are in the air!

Here is the solution to stopping this behavior: Never give in to a beggar! You are rewarding the dog for sitting pretty, jumping up, whining and rubbing his nose into you by giving him that glorious reward—food. By ignoring the dog, you will (eventually) force the behavior into extinction. Note that the behavior likely gets worse before it disappears, so be sure there are not any "softies" in the family who will give in to little "Oliver" every time he whimpers, "More, please."

Goldens can become beggars. They will put on their most enchanting face and whine until you share your food with them.

SEPARATION ANXIETY

Your Golden Retriever may howl, whine or otherwise vocalize his displeasure at your leaving the house and his being left alone. This is a normal case of separation anxiety, and there are things that can be done to eliminate this problem. Your dog needs to learn that he will be fine on his own for a while and that he will not wither away if he is not attended to every minute of the day. In fact, constant attention can lead to separation anxiety in the first place. If you are endlessly coddling and cooing over your

Goldens get lonely without almost constant attention from their masters. Owning two Goldens can reduce the stress of separation anxiety, though the dogs will still keenly anticipate your return home.

dog, he will come to expect this from you all of the time and it will be more traumatic for him when you are not there. Obviously, you enjoy spending time with your dog, and he thrives on your love and attention. However, it should not become a dependent relationship in which he is heartbroken without you.

One thing you can do to minimize separation anxiety is to make your entrances and exits as low-key as possible. Do not give your dog a long drawn-out goodbye, and do not lavish him with hugs and kisses when you return. This is giving in to

the attention that he craves, and it will only make him miss it more when you are away. Another thing you can try is to give your dog a treat when you leave; this will not only keep

I'M HOME!

Dogs left alone for varying lengths of time may often react wildly when you return. Sometimes they run, jump, bite, chew, tear things apart, wet themselves, gobble their food or behave in other undisciplined manners. Allow them to calm down before greeting them or they will consider your attention as a reward for their antics.

Golden puppies want to please you. If you can make your intentions clear to your puppy, he will obey you and be delighted that you are pleased.

SEPARATION ANXIETY

The number of dogs who suffer from separation anxiety is on the rise as more and more pet owners find themselves at work all day. New attention is being paid to this problem, which is especially hard to diagnose since it is only evident when the dog is alone. Research is currently being done to help educate dog owners about separation anxiety and about how they can help minimize this problem in their dogs.

him occupied and keep his mind off the fact that you just left, but it will also help him associate your leaving with a pleasant experience.

You may have to accustom your dog to being left alone in intervals, much like when you introduced your pup to his crate. Of course, when your dog starts whimpering as you approach the door, your first instinct will be to run to him and comfort him, but do not do

it! Really—eventually he will adjust and be just fine if you take it in small steps. His anxiety stems from being placed in an unfamiliar situation; by familiarizing him with being alone, he will learn that he is okay. That is not to say you should purposely leave your dog home alone, but the dog needs to know that while he can depend on you for his care, you do not have to be by his side 24 hours a day.

When the dog is alone in the house, he should be confined to his crate or a designated dog-proof area of the house. This should be the area in which he sleeps and already feels comfortable so he will feel more at ease when he is alone. This is just one of the many examples in which a crate is an invaluable tool for you and your dog, and another reinforcement of why your dog should view his crate as a "happy" place, a place of his own.

COPROPHAGIA

Feces eating is, to us humans, one of the most disgusting behaviors that their dog could engage in, yet to the dog it is perfectly normal. It is hard for us to understand why a dog would want to eat his own feces. He could be seeking certain nutrients that are missing from his diet, he could

be just plain hungry or he could be attracted by the pleasing (to a dog) scent. While coprophagia most often refers to the dog's eating his own feces, a dog may eat that of another animal as well if he comes across it. Vets

PHARMACEUTICAL FIXES

There are two drugs specifically designed to treat mental problems in dogs. About 7 million dogs each year are destroyed because owners can no longer tolerate their dogs' behavior, according to Nicholas Dodman, a specialist in animal behavior at Tufts University in Massachusetts.

The first drug, Clomicalm, is prescribed for dogs suffering from separation anxiety, which is said to cause them to react when left alone by barking, chewing their owners' belongings, drooling copiously, or defecating or urinating inside the home.

The second drug, Anipryl, is recommended for canine cognitive dysfunction or "old dog syndrome," a mental deterioration that comes with age. Such dogs often seem to forget that they were housebroken and where their food bowls are, and they may even fail to recognize their owners.

A tremendous human-animal-bonding relationship is established with all dogs, particularly senior dogs. This precious relationship deteriorates when the dog does not recognize his master. The drug can restore the bond and make senior dogs feel more like their old selves.

have found that diets with a low digestibility, containing relatively low levels of fiber and high levels of starch, increase coprophagia. Therefore, high-fiber diets may decrease the likelihood of dogs' eating feces. Both the consistency of the stool (how firm it feels in the dog's mouth) and the presence of undigested nutrients increase the likelihood. Dogs often find the stool of cats and horses more palatable than that of other dogs. Once the dog develops diarrhea from eating his own feces, he will likely quit this distasteful habit, since dogs tend to prefer eating harder feces.

To discourage this behavior, first make sure that the food you are feeding your dog is nutritionally complete and that he is getting enough food. If changes in his diet do not seem to work, and no medical cause can be found, you will have to modify the behavior through environmental control before it becomes a habit. There are some tricks you can try, such as adding an unpleasant-tasting substance to the feces to make them unpalatable or adding something to the dog's food, which will make it unpleasant-tasting after it passes through the dog. The best way to prevent your dog from eating his stool is to make it unavailable—clean up after he eliminates and remove any stool from the yard. If it is not there, he cannot eat it.

Never reprimand the dog for stool eating, as this rarely impresses the dog. Vets recommend distracting the dog while he is in the act of stool eating. Another option is to muzzle the dog when he is in the yard to relieve himself; this usually is effective within 30 to 60 days. Coprophagia is seen most frequently in pups 6 to 12 months of age, and usually disappears around the dog's first birthday.

Although Goldens are super-affectionate, it's better not to engage in mouth-to-mouth moments.

When you purchase your Golden Retriever, you will make it clear to the breeder whether you want one just as a lovable companion and pet, or if you hope to be buying a Golden Retriever with show prospects. No reputable breeder will sell you a young puppy and tell you that it is *definitely* of show quality, for so much can go wrong during the early months of a puppy's development. If you plan to show, what you will hopefully have acquired is a puppy with "show potential."

To the novice, exhibiting a Golden Retriever in the show ring may look easy, but it takes a lot of hard work and devotion to do top winning at a show such as the prestigious Westminster Kennel Club dog show, not to mention a little luck too!

Ribbons, medals and trophies bedeck the walls of famous dog homes. Winning in the show ring indicates that a breeder has been successful in his program.

AKC GROUPS
For showing purposes, the American Kennel Club divides its recognized breeds into seven groups: Sporting Dogs, Hounds, Working Dogs, Terriers, Toys, Non-Sporting Dogs and Herding Dogs.

The first concept that the canine novice learns when watching a dog show is that each dog first competes against members of his own breed. Once the judge has selected the best member of each breed (Best of Breed), that chosen dog will compete with other dogs in his

group. Finally, the dogs chosen first in each group will compete for Best in Show.

The second concept that you must understand is that the dogs are not actually compared against one another. The judge compares each dog against his breed standard, the American Kennel Club (AKC)-approved written description of the ideal breed specimen. While some early breed standards were indeed based on specific dogs that were

famous or popular, many dedicated enthusiasts say that a perfect specimen, as described in the standard, has never walked into a show ring, has never been bred and, to the woe of dog breeders around the globe, does not exist. Breeders intention of competing with your Golden, a specialty is like a festival for lovers of the breed who congregate to share their favorite topic: Goldens! Clubs also send out newsletters, and some organize training days and seminars in order

Competing in an all-breed show with your Golden Retriever is an exciting prospect. It takes many years of experience to become a competent, consistent dog handler.

attempt to get as close to this ideal as possible with every litter, but theoretically the "perfect" dog is so elusive that it is impossible.

If you are interested in exploring the world of dog showing, your best bet is to join your local breed club or the national parent club, which is the Golden Retriever Club of America. These clubs often host both regional and national specialties, shows only for Golden Retrievers, which can include conformation as well as obedience and field trials. Even if you have no

that people may learn more about their chosen breed. To locate the breed club closest to you, contact the AKC, which furnishes the rules and regulations for all of these events plus general dog registration and other basic requirements of dog ownership.

The AKC offers three kinds of conformation shows: an all-breed show (for all AKC-recognized breeds), a specialty show (for one breed only, usually sponsored by the parent club) and a Group show (for all breeds in the Group).

BECOMING A CHAMPION

An official AKC champion of record requires that a dog accumulate 15 points under three different judges, including two "majors" under different judges. Points are awarded based on the number of dogs entered into competition, varying from breed to breed and place to place. A win of three, four or five points is considered a "major." The AKC assigns a schedule of points annually to adjust to the variations that accompany a breed's popularity and the population of a given area.

For a dog to become an AKC champion of record, the dog must accumulate 15 points at the shows from at least three different judges, including two "majors." A "major" is defined as a three-, four- or five-point win. The number of points per win is determined by the number of dogs entered in the show on that day. Depending on the breed, the number of points that are awarded varies. In a breed as popular as the Golden Retriever, more dogs are needed to rack up the points. At any dog show, only one dog and one bitch of each breed can win points.

Dog showing does not offer "co-ed" classes. Dogs and bitches never compete against each other in the classes. Non-champion dogs are called "class dogs" because they compete in one of five classes. Dogs are entered in a particular class depending on their ages and previous show wins. To begin, there

The American Kennel Club encourages Junior Handlers to become involved in dog shows. There is no better education for the next generation of dog people.

Golden Retrievers are popular show dogs around the world. This Golden is an accomplished champion from Europe.

is the Puppy Class (for 6- to 9-month-olds and for 9- to 12-month-olds); this class is followed by the Novice Class (for dogs that have not won any first prizes except in the Puppy Class or three first prizes in the Novice Class and have not accumulated any points toward their champion title); the Bred-by-Exhibitor Class (for dogs handled by their breeders or handled by one of the breeder's immediate family); the American-bred Class (for dogs bred in the USA!); and the Open Class (for any dog that is not a champion).

The judge at the show begins judging the Puppy Class, first dogs and then bitches, and proceeds through the classes. The judge places his winners first through fourth in each class. In the next-level class, the Winners Class, the first-place winners of each class compete with one another to determine Winners Dog and

Winners Bitch. The judge also places a Reserve Winners Dog and Reserve Winners Bitch, which could be awarded the points in the

SHOW ETIQUETTE
Just like with anything else, there is a certain etiquette to the show ring that can only be learned through experience. Showing your dog can be quite intimidating to you as a novice when it seems as if everyone else knows what he's doing. You can familiarize yourself with ring procedure beforehand by taking a class to prepare you and your dog for conformation showing or by talking with an experienced handler. When you are in the ring, listen and pay attention to the judge and follow his/her directions. Remember, even the most skilled handlers had to start somewhere. Keep it up and you too will become a proficient handler before too long!

Showing is hard work for the dogs, too!

JUNIOR SHOWMANSHIP

For budding dog handlers, ages 10 to 18 years, Junior Showmanship competitions are an excellent training ground for the next generation of dog professionals. Owning and caring for a dog are wonderful methods of teaching children responsibility, and Junior Showmanship builds upon that foundation. Juniors learn by grooming, handling and training their dogs, and the quality of junior's presentation of the dog (and himself) is evaluated by a licensed judge.

case of a disqualification. The Winners Dog and Winners Bitch are the two that are awarded the points for the breed, then compete with any champions of record entered in the show. The judge reviews the Winners Dog, Winners Bitch and all of the champions to select his Best of Breed. The Best of Winners is selected between the

There are many obstacles which must be overcome in agility trials for dogs. These trials are almost always very competitive, but also a lot of fun.

Winners Dog and Winners Bitch. Were one of these two to be selected Best of Breed, it would automatically be named Best of Winners as well. Finally the judge selects his Best of Opposite Sex to the Best of Breed winner.

At a Group show or all-breed show, the Best of Breed winners from each breed then compete against one another in their respective groups for Group One through Group Four. The judge compares each Best of Breed to his breed standard, and the dog that most closely lives up to the ideal for his breed is selected as Group One. Finally, all seven group winners (from the Sporting Group, Toy

Golden Retrievers participating in the Parade of Tartans are favorites of the Scottish and Irish. This event took place in Colorado.

Group, Hound Group, etc.) compete for Best in Show.

To find out about dog shows in your area, you can subscribe to the American Kennel Club's monthly magazine, the *American Kennel Gazette* and the accompanying *Events Calendar.* You can also look in your local newspaper for advertisements for dog shows in your area or go on the Internet to the AKC's website, www.akc.org.

If your Golden Retriever is six months of age or older and registered with the AKC, you can enter him in a dog show where the breed is offered classes. Provided that your Golden Retriever does not have a disqualifying fault, he can compete. Only unaltered dogs can be entered in a dog show, so if you

MEET THE AKC

The American Kennel Club is the main governing body of the dog sport in the United States. Founded in 1884, the AKC consists of 500 or more independent dog clubs plus 4,500 affiliate clubs, all of which follow AKC rules and regulations. Additionally, the AKC maintains a registry for pure-bred dogs in the US and works to preserve the integrity of dog sport and its continuation in the country. Over 1,000,000 dogs are registered each year, representing about 150 recognized breeds. There are over 15,000 competitive events held annually for which over 2,000,000 dogs enter to participate. Dogs compete to earn over 40 different titles, from Champion to Companion Dog to Master Agility Champion.

Golden Retrievers can retrieve small birds and well as large game fowl. This dog has retrieved a pigeon.

have spayed or neutered your Golden Retriever, you cannot compete in conformation shows. The reason for this is simple. Dog shows are the main forum to prove which representatives of a breed are worthy of being bred. Only dogs that have achieved championships—the AKC "seal of approval" for quality in pure-bred

CLUB CONTACTS

You can get information about dog shows from kennel clubs:

American Kennel Club
5580 Centerview Dr., Raleigh, NC 27606-3390
www.akc.org

United Kennel Club
100 E. Kilgore Road, Kalamazoo, MI 49002
www.ukcdogs.com

Canadian Kennel Club
89 Skyway Ave., Suite 100, Etobicoke, Ontario
M9W 6R4, Canada
www.ckc.ca

The Kennel Club
1-5 Clarges St., Piccadilly,
London W1Y 8AB, UK
www.the-kennel-club.org.uk

dogs—should be bred. Altered dogs, however, can participate in other AKC events such as obedience trials and the Canine Good Citizen program.

OBEDIENCE TRIALS

Obedience trials in the US trace back to the early 1930s when organized obedience training was developed to demonstrate how well dog and owner could work together. The pioneer of obedience trials is Mrs. Helen Whitehouse Walker, a Standard Poodle fancier, who designed a series of exercises after the Associated, Sheep, Police Army Dog Society of Great Britain. Since the days of Mrs. Walker, obedience trials have grown by leaps and bounds, and today there are over 2,000 trials held in the US every year, with more than 100,000 dogs competing. Any AKC-registered dog can enter an obedience trial, regardless of conformational disqualifications or neutering.

Obedience trials are divided into three levels of progressive difficulty. At the first level, the Novice, dogs compete for the title Companion Dog (CD); at the intermediate level, the Open, dogs compete for the title Companion Dog Excellent (CDX); and at the advanced level, the Utility, dogs compete for the title Utility Dog (UD). Classes are sub-divided into "A" (for beginners) and "B" (for more experienced handlers). A perfect score at any level is 200, and

a dog must score 170 or better to earn a "leg," of which three are needed to earn the title. To earn points, the dog must score more than 50% of the available points in each exercise; the possible points range from   20 to 40.

Each level consists of a different set of exercises. In the Novice level, the dog must heel on and off lead, come, long sit, long down and stand for examination. These skills are the basic ones required for a well-behaved "Companion Dog." The Open level requires that the dog perform the same exercises above, but without a leash, for extended lengths of time, as well as retrieve a dumbbell, broad jump and drop on recall. In the Utility level, dogs must perform ten difficult exercises, including scent discrimination, hand signals for basic commands, directed jump and directed retrieve.

Once a dog has earned the UD title, he can compete with other proven obedience dogs for the coveted title of Utility Dog Excellent (UDX), which requires that the dog win "legs" in ten shows. Utility Dogs who earn "legs" in Open B and Utility B earn points toward their Obedience Trial Champion title. In 1977, the title Obedience Trial Champion (OTCh.) was established by the AKC. To become an OTCh., a dog needed to earn 100 points, which requires three first places in Open B and Utility under three different judges. The first dog to earn the OTCh. title was a Golden

Retriever named Moreland's Golden Tonk, owned by Russ Klippie.

AGILITY TRIALS
Having had its origins in the UK back in 1977, AKC agility had its official beginning in the US in August 1994, when the first licensed agility trials were held. The AKC allows all registered breeds (including Miscellaneous Class breeds) to participate, providing the dog is 12 months of age or older. Agility is designed so that the handler demonstrates how well the dog can work at his side. The handler directs his dog over an obstacle course that includes jumps as well as tires, the dog walk, weave poles, pipe tunnels, collapsed tunnels, etc. While working his way through the course, the dog must keep one eye and ear on the handler and the rest of his body on the course. The handler gives verbal commands and hand signals to guide the dog through the course.

Goldens act like a bunch of kids having their first swim of the season. Goldens love water and you can take advantage of this natural trait by using them as hunting dogs.

TRACKING

Any dog is capable of tracking, using its nose to follow a trail. Tracking tests are exciting and competitive ways to test your Golden Retriever's ability to search and rescue. The AKC started tracking tests in 1937, when the first AKC-licensed test took place as part of the Utility level at an obedience trial. Ten years later in 1947, the AKC offered the first title, Tracking Dog (TD). In 1950, the first Golden Retriever to earn the TD was Featherquest Trigger, owned by Marjorie Perry. A chip off the old block, Trigger was the son of Goldwood Toby UD, the first Golden to earn the UD title in an obedience trial. It was not until 1980 that the AKC added the Tracking Dog Excellent title (TDX), which was followed by the Versatile Surface Tracking title (VST) in 1995. The title Champion Tracker (CT) is awarded to a dog who has earned all three titles.

FIELD TRIALS

Field trials are offered to the retrievers, pointers and spaniel breeds of the Sporting Group as well as to the Beagles, Dachshunds and Bassets of the Hound Group. The purpose of field trials is to demonstrate a dog's ability to perform its original purpose in the field. The events vary depending on the type of dog, but in all trials dogs compete against one another for placement and for points toward their Field Champion (FC) titles. The first Golden to become a Field Champion in the US was FC Rip, owned by Paul Bakewell III, this back in 1939.

Retriever field trials, designed to simulate "an ordinary day's shoot," are popular and likely the most demanding of these trials. Dogs must "mark" the location of downed feather game and then return the birds to the shooter. Successful dogs are able to "mark" the downed game by remembering where the bird fell as well as by the correct use of the wind and terrain. Dogs are tested both on land and water. Difficulty levels are based on the number of birds downed as well as the number of "blind retrieves" (where a bird is placed away from the view of the dog and the handler directs the dog by the use of hand signals and verbal commands). The term "Non-Slip" retriever, often applied to these trials, refers to a dog that is steady at the handler's side until commanded to go. Every field trial includes four stakes of increasing levels of difficulty. Each stake is judged by a team of two judges who look for many natural abilities including steadiness, courage, style, control and training.

HUNTING TESTS

Hunting tests are not competitive like field trials, and participating dogs are judged against a standard like in a conformation show. The first hunting tests were devised by the North American Hunting Retriever Association (NAHRA) as an alternative to field trials for

retriever owners to appreciate their dogs' natural innate ability in the field without the expense and pressure of formal field trials. The intent of hunting tests is the same as that of field trials, to test the dog's ability in a simulated hunting scenario.

The AKC instituted its hunting tests in June 1985, and popularity has grown tremendously. The AKC offers three titles at hunting tests, Junior Hunter (JH), Senior Hunter (SH) and Master Hunter (MH). Each title requires that the dog earn qualifying "legs" at the tests: the JH requiring four; the SH, five; and the MH, six. In addition to the AKC, the United Kennel Club also offers hunting tests through its affiliate club, the Hunting Retriever Club, Inc. (HRC), which began the tests in 1984.

RESCUE PERSONNEL
On the tracking course, Golden Retrievers earn tracking titles that rival the hound breeds known for their scenting prowess. This has a practical function as well...that famous Golden nose also works in search-and-rescue operations around the world. During every international disaster, from mudslides to earthquakes to terrorist bomb sites, Goldens join the ranks of rescue personnel to help find victims buried beneath the mud or rubble.

INDEX

Page numbers in **boldface** indicate illustrations.